A
SURGEON'S DOMAIN

Dr. Bernheim is an American and is Associate Professor of Surgery at The Johns Hopkins Medical School and Visiting Surgeon to The Johns Hopkins Hospital, Baltimore, U.S.A.

The views and opinions herein expressed are his own and do not purport to express those of his colleagues.

A SURGEON'S DOMAIN

by

BERTRAM M. BERNHEIM, M.D.

THE WORLD'S WORK (1913) LTD
KINGSWOOD :: SURREY

FIRST PUBLISHED 1949

x760284511

vc.

PRINTED IN GREAT BRITAIN
AT THE WINDMILL PRESS
KINGSWOOD, SURREY

CONTENTS

FOREWORD

THIS BOOK WILL BE CONCERNED WITH SURGERY AND THE story of the men who operate on you when you get surgically sick or have a serious accident. There is adventure and excitement in surgery; in more ways than one it's like a major sport. Perhaps that horrifies you and disturbs your sensibilities; but I'm going to set things down as they look to me, and they don't look the way a lot of people think they ought to.

I'm going to do something else—or try to. I'm going to put certain experiences in story form in order to highlight points that otherwise might be lost. Certain of my friends say you can't have a book that's part one thing and part another, but I'm not especially interested in good form in book writing or in anything else. I'm interested in explaining certain things of a medical nature that need airing, and if that can be accomplished best by unorthodox methods, does it matter?

I shall have to project myself into the picture, for by the very fact of not thinking things through at the beginning of my career, and perhaps not having anyone to advise me, I was to have an experience not only different but broader than that of most of my contemporaries; and though the cards at times seemed stacked against me, I always found a new and illuminating viewpoint, one that made life and work worth while. I couldn't tell of men and deeds and the suffering sick and all that goes to make up the surgeon's life if I didn't give first-hand accounts, nor could I tell convincingly of the peculiar flush of satisfaction a man gets from good operating—and the crushing sense of futility that comes from bad operating—if I had not experienced both.

Just what I wished for myself in the beginning isn't clear, other than that I soon knew I wanted to operate. The men I saw doing it seemed so calm and self-possessed in the face of ghastly wounds and blood and suffering that the whole business both intrigued and disturbed my imagination. I knew I had to try my hand at it. Furthermore, these men appeared to be buoyed up by their work in a strange sort of way and they never seemed to get enough of it. They loved to do different kinds of operations and some were known to be better at one kind than another. It was a little odd, men actually liking to operate on people.

It never occurred to me that one day I might be chief surgeon of a big hospital and have the duty of choosing house officers and teaching them how to operate. "Private practitioner of surgery" was vaguely in my mind, and that's about all. I was too young and too unlearned in things medical and the world in particular to have such aspirations. Another dampener to latent enthusiasm was the thought that I might well be thrown out at the end of the third year because of my mediocre work in the medical school, a thought that made me glad to get away from Baltimore the moment I got my diploma. Like many other medical students just become doctors, then and now, I was all mixed up without knowing it, and since nobody took the trouble to straighten me out—if indeed anyone knew of my perturbation—I had to work my way out as best I could.

For permission to reprint two of the chapters, "Learning the Job" and "In the Dispensary", acknowledgment is made to the *Saturday Evening Post*, where they first appeared as "The Surgeon Learns His Job" and "What a Doctor Sees in You", respectively. It was the response to these articles that led me to undertake this book. In it you will find a number of things that both surgeons and patients—and who isn't one or the other?—have or should have on their minds. You will also find, I hope, that there is more to surgery than operations.

BERTRAM M. BERNHEIM.

Baltimore, Maryland.

1

GENERALLY SPEAKING

SURGEONS ARE AMONG THE LEAST EXPENDABLE OF MEN.
Few people realise it, but it is so. It takes long years of
constant application to make them: in the very nature of
things, there are no child prodigies among them as there
are in music, literature, mathematics, hog-calling, and a
host of other careers. In times of stress, by intensive training you can turn out bucketfuls of aviators and military
men and sea captains—perhaps not the best, but men of
usefulness (and this is not said in disparagement)—but
not surgeons. You can't make good physicians, either;
but even they can be had faster than surgeons. The art
of operating has to be hand taught and it has to be
individual; none of the mass production, assembly-line
methods will do, with classes all through the day and far
into the night. Each man must actually use the knife himself; he must be brought to it carefully, nursed along and
guided; he will have to do hundreds of operations—yes,
and make mistakes—before he's any good, and that takes
time and patience and understanding. It costs something,
too, and I don't mean money! Maybe the succeeding pages
will show you how it's done.

Operating is gruelling work for the most part and it is
just as well that the surgeon be not too thin-skinned. It
follows, therefore, that, like the combat aviators of modern
war who are chosen for their tender youth and uninhibited
nervous systems, the would-be surgeons do best and are
least squeamish if taken in their formative years when

their minds and nerves are young. This doesn't mean that youngsters have to be shanghaied into surgery or even persuaded to go into it. On the contrary, if they listen to some of the older men many are dissuaded because of the long hard row so vividly portrayed. They all make their own independent choice and it's hard to say just how they come to a decision. I should say that money plays the smallest role. Even though it is commonly supposed that surgeons make great fortunes, only the few do. The average surgeon makes little more than a good living, and many of them don't even do that. It would be fatuous to deny, however, that some are influenced by the lure of wealth coupled with ideas of the surgeon's glamour and possibly easier life, his concern with bigger things—all over-emphasised by the uninitiated.

But young men like adventure and excitement above all things, and no sooner do medical students get set to go during the very first week of the first year when lots of them make for the benches of surgical amphitheatres to see with their own eyes what an operation—that gory, mysterious thing they've heard so much about—is like. Authorities forbid it, hospitals decry it, upper class-men frown on it, but nothing stops the trek; and though the juveniles sometimes have to resort to infiltration tactics, all who wish to, sooner or later have their curiosity gratified— usually sooner. Right then and there some men are so sickened and disgusted that they lose forever whatever desire they may have had for surgery; while others come away thrilled to the bone and so exhilarated and excited that they can hardly wait until the time comes for them to handle the knife. The white-clad doctors and nurses intent on their work; the gowned, gloved, and masked surgeons actually using knife and scissors on human beings and not being afraid or nervous; the beautiful teamwork; the calm and quiet of the operating-room, the odd, sweetish odour, and, yes, the blood—not much but some—to say nothing of the anæsthetised patient; the brilliant white light spotted particularly on the operative field—all these things fire the imagination and create the fever.

I was months getting over my first experience; the classmate who was responsible for it was affected for life. This thin, reddish-haired, slow-spoken, humorous southerner who said surgery was in his very bones asked me to take the usual journey to the operating-room with him. We had met only a few days before, but it was not that which deterred me. I was afraid. The dissecting rooms were bad enough—in fact, almost more than I could bear—and the idea of seeing an operation on a living person floored me.

"Time enough when the third year comes," I said. "What's the hurry?"

"Ah'm a-gonna be a surgeon," he replied in his southern drawl, "an' ah cain't wait to see what it's like. Ain't you gonna be a surgeon?"

"I don't know what I'm going to be right now, but if surgery's anything like dissecting and if the smell in operating-rooms is as bad as this is in here, that's what I ain't a-gonna be!" As a gentleman from Kentucky, I liked to lapse into the lingo myself.

Roy laughed and said: "Come on! Ah found the way."

"No," I replied, and was adamant—for four days. Then I fell. The scoundrel kept telling me what the other fellows had seen, how wonderful it all was, how they would gather in groups to talk about "the big, bull-necked guy" who stood up to the table and cut hell out of patient after patient without batting an eyelid—Finney was his name—until the lure was too great and one hot morning the two

of us stumbled through devious corridors and up dark
stairways to reach the very topmost benches. It was an old
wooden semi-circular amphitheatre, of the type that now
is almost obsolete, and the air was close and heavy with a
sickening kind of sweetish odour that the other boys said
was ether. It didn't make me exactly sick, but I was
nervous and wished I'd never come. Roy sat there grinning and patted me on the knee, but for once he had little
to say. An old wooden operating-table, bare of anything
but pads and a white sheet, stood down below in the
middle of the floor, and around it was a narrow half-
circular metal table covered with a sheet, on top of which
was one tray after another of shining instruments. I
couldn't believe there were so many surgical instruments
in the world. When I asked Roy if he thought they'd use
all those things on one patient, he just gulped and shook
his head. A young gowned and gloved doctor was calmly
sorting out the instruments.

Soon a stocky, broad-shouldered, handsome man—they
didn't wear face masks then—came in and began to slip
on gown and gloves. They said he was the "Finney guy".
A minute later they wheeled in a man who was being
given ether by the old-fashioned method (a cone into
which the anæsthetic was poured or dropped). Before you
could say Jack Robinson two other husky fellows came out
of nowhere—orderlies, they called them—and lifted the
patient from stretcher to table. They did everything non-
chalantly and none too tenderly to my way of thinking,
but no one seemed to mind, and who was I to complain?

The surgeon began to talk in a loud, firm voice, but I
couldn't understand most of the words he used. The boys
said he was giving the history. Not Roy but the other boys,
of whom there were several. Roy was quiet and, to my eye,

looked paler than usual. The "Finney guy" talked awfully long, it seemed to me, and even when another doctor and a nurse had spread sheets and towels over the patient and stood there doing nothing, he was still talking. The man, I guessed, had a lot wrong with him. I noticed that the doctor and nurse had left both groins exposed. I don't remember what was in my mind, but I was wholly unprepared for what happened next.

While he was still talking, Finney, who, they all said, was such a great surgeon,* stepped up to the operating-table, held out his gloved right hand, had the flat handle of a glistening knife slapped into it, and forthwith made a long, straight cut in the right groin and immediately went down deep. Blood flowed, assistants hurriedly began putting on a lot of instruments the boys said were clamps to stop it. Finney never stopped talking or cutting, and man, it was a sight. My stomach turned over and Roy's face turned green. But Finney, not satisfied with the damage he'd already done, turned to the man's left groin and laid that wide open. The boys said he took out the glands because the man had a cancer, but Roy and I didn't see that part of it. With one accord we rushed out and down the steps for the fresh, cool air and Roy gave up his breakfast on reaching the sidewalk. I just sat on the kerbstone, holding my head. When we both came to, Roy said: "Ah'm cured. No surgery for me. How 'bout you?"

"I don't know about surgery, Roy, but if you have any more brilliant ideas of visiting other parts of this hospital, please keep them to yourself!"

After that I didn't go near an operation for two years—

* John M. T. Finney—later one of America's foremost surgeons but even then well on his way. In World War I he became Chief Consulting Surgeon of the A.E.F., having gone to France as Chief of the Hopkins Unit from which he was very early detached.

not until the third year came and it was required. Roy didn't, either, true to his word. In after years he went into pathology, where he made quite a name for himself.

There is no royal road to surgery. On the contrary, it is hard, rocky, tortuous, and all uphill. When I began, there was a wrong and a right way, but there isn't now. There's only the right way, and that has come about because high medical authority has decreed that no man can become a surgeon unless he serves an apprenticeship of two to four years in a hospital of recognised worth and standing. Since that necessity wasn't so generally recognised then as now, and since a pretty girl had promised to be my bride (hospitals of that day frowned on married internes), I did it the hard way and never became the easy operator that my friends did who took the usual course. I never became as skilled, either, but chance and the friendship of the "Finney guy" gave me a firm grounding which, coupled with a fair degree of common sense, saved the day for me—and maybe some of my patients.

My struggle gave me an insight into other men's tribulations and later on made me tolerant of the shortcomings of younger men. Instead of taking two to four years after graduation to become a surgeon, it took me nearly ten, even more, and meant my haunting the operating-rooms—not only of Baltimore but of every town and village I visited at home or abroad. The dividends that experience was to pay in knowledge of people, sick and well, and of hospitals and things medical, did not come home to me till years later. But I may as well confess that the road travelled was never arduous. My natural inquisitiveness and liking for the unusual and different made it interesting—and my love of people and adventure.

If, after graduation, I had been good enough to make

the Hopkins hospital it might have been different, but only the first ten men of the class could be internes and that let me out. I did take competitive examinations for a Brooklyn hospital but failed and gave up. So instead of becoming an interne and later perhaps a resident and easing my way into surgery by orthodox channels, I married the girl and went to Germany which at that time (1905) was reputed to have the greatest surgeons and the best surgery in the world. I planned to spend three years studying and learning their methods, after which I would be ready for practice back home. Unfortunately it did not work out that way, chiefly because of my dislike for everything German, even the language. One year was too long and I could hardly wait to get back home.

Home was Kentucky, of course; but I hung around Baltimore for six months attending clinics and brushing up, hoping to get a post at Johns Hopkins but failed. Then I reluctantly accepted the position of assistant to a prominent surgeon in Louisville and, gathering up my little family, went out to meet the world.

The early mistake of not becoming a surgical house officer was to be nearly fatal to my chances of becoming a surgeon. The surgeon with whom I became associated was very kind and so were all the other doctors, some of them boyhood friends. But he couldn't let me operate on his private patients even if I had had ability and training, and he didn't have the authority to let me "do" cases under supervision on his service at the city hospital. Such operations as he did not do himself went to the house men. All I did was to assist in his private work and do an occasional wound closure. Even when we travelled to outlying towns and villages for operation in people's homes, as we did occasionally, I got nothing out of it except the chance to move furniture to make way for kitchen tables to be used for operating purposes and to boil up instruments on stoves littered with cooking pots and pans.

At that it was a rewarding experience, and never for one moment have I regretted this opportunity to meet intimately my fellow Kentuckians. They were and still are a simple, kindly folk of generous instincts and limited education, unlearned, even perhaps uninterested, in the ways and customs of the outside world; but they were hard-working, self-respecting people who asked no charity and minded their own business. Incidentally, they saw to it that you minded yours, but as long as you did they welcomed you as a friend and offered generous hospitality. They helped each other in sorrow and trouble; they gathered together for parties; they liked nothing better than to have you join them; and if you chewed a bit of tobacco and could take their "mountain dew" without strangling, so much the better.

Altogether I practised one year in Kentucky. All in all it was a year well spent; but I wasn't getting on in surgery and by that time I had been bitten by the bug of research and the higher medicine. There weren't laboratories or teachers available for experimental work, since Louisville was not then the medical centre it is today, so again I intensively scouted the situation in Baltimore and came up with a non-paying job in the Hopkins Surgical Dispensary. This was given me by Dr. Finney, who had charge of that department, and I have always felt that he did me one of the greatest favours an older doctor can do a younger one. He gave me a chance to work—not operate, just work. You don't operate in dispensaries, or operate very little. You do little things like opening boils, sewing up small accidental wounds and such, but for the most part you examine patients and take histories and dress leg ulcers and sores of all kinds. That in itself is a major opportunity, but if in addition the dispensary is connected with a teaching institution where the staff instructs students, it can be a boon for the young doctor who has the sense to trail along and look and listen.

As a student I used to get fed up with the Hopkins, chiefly, I think, because much of what went on was over my head. Somehow or other my mentality balked at the rudiments of medicine and I became terribly depressed. Moreover, the elegance and the culture of the place bored me. But I had come back—I always came back to the Hopkins—and liked it.

I think they liked me, too—but with reservations, because I was a thorn in their side with my queer (to them) ideas and embarrassing questions. They had never known a fellow who seriousy aspired to surgery through unorthodox channels and didn't quite know what to make of him. Meanwhile I was undergoing the unusual experience of having my cake and eating it, too. That is, I had got the girl and was in process of getting the surgery— without ever becoming a house officer!

It will thus be apparent that my entry into surgery was by the back door, so to speak, where you see things that are not meant to be displayed, where worn-out stuff that ought to be discarded is stored away or maybe left lying around, but where much of the best talk goes on and lots of the carousing. Those who enter by the front door see little of this and consequently miss a great deal that is of deep significance. When things did break for me eventually —the friendship of John M. T. Finney, the opportunity to do research work under Harvey Cushing, the chance to get into the new and then untried field of blood transfusion, the outbreak of World War I and participation therein—I had my rewards; but mine was an uneven course of many ups and downs, wonderfully illuminating and at times exciting but decidedly back-doorish. I propose to tell something of it and to present pictures of surgeons operating, people being operated on, young doctors being brought for the first time to operate on human beings, their trials and temptations and agonies, the talk and chatter that go on between surgeon and assistants, sometimes the sudden hush that spells danger, even tragedy.

I may even digress a bit and draw conclusions and peer into the future.

2

BRINGING UP THE CHIEF

IT TOOK A WAR REALLY TO GET ME STARTED IN SURGERY, BUT
since that didn't happen until 1917—nine years after I
returned to Baltimore—it will be clear what a struggle I'd
been having. Fortune hadn't exactly overlooked me during
these years, but she hadn't sent me in the direction I
wanted to go. In the Hopkins laboratories I had the good
fortune to devise a little tube which launched me in the
new and fascinating field of blood transfusion; but the
surgery connected with it was insignificant for practical
purposes. To compensate I formed the habit of attending
Dr. Finney's operative clinic each Thursday at the Union
Protestant Infirmary, where an incident occurred that was
as unusual as it was exciting.

It was a blustery, chilly, overcast morning, and as usual a
big gallery was on hand. I was somewhat on edge because
a femoral aneurism was on the list of cases to be done and
the great man had instructed me to prepare and have ready
for use one of Halsted's recently devised instruments for
applying a constricting aluminium band. Dr. Halsted, renowned professor at the Hopkins though he was, worked
alongside his humblest assistants in the laboratory and
that is how I had come to see and become familiar with
the new apparatus. I had even tried it on a dog, but never
on a human being. Dr. Finney hadn't, either; but it was
simplicity itself, and if the thing was prepared, there would
be no difficulty.

Two or three other operations preceded the aneurism (saccular dilatation of a blood vessel), but finally Dr. Finney came to it and everything was going well when suddenly the operating-room supervisor hurried in, tapped the doctor lightly on the shoulder, whispered something in his ear, and presto! the whole picture changed. He stopped operating and stood there as if he were stunned, knife poised in the air. Obviously, something serious had happened but none of us knew or suspected what it was so we kept quiet. The doctor resumed his operation without saying anything, but again he stopped. Turning to the group, he said: "There's been a bad wreck up beyond Harrisburg and a relative of mine is among the badly injured. They want me to come immediately."

Without another word he went back to his operating, one or two of the onlookers gave a nervous cough, but no one said anything. Then the doctor's right-hand man, big, heavy Omar Pancoast, who was always present if possible at the Thursday exercises, asked: "Would you like me to scrub up and finish this case, sir?"

The doctor didn't answer immediately, but it was plain that he was dawdling with the operation—and thinking. Finally, his mind evidently made up, he threw down his instruments and, stepping away from the table, said: "I can't finish this case, but I don't want you to go ahead with it, Pancoast. Call Chuck Bond—he was here a few minutes ago—and have him take over." Bells began to tap out the doctor's call, and nurses, orderlies, and doctors dashed out to hurry Chuck in.

"I want you to go with me, Pancoast," Dr. Finney said as the nurses began to divest him of gown, face mask, and gloves. "While I'm changing my clothes I'd like you to get in touch with the local railroad superintendent and have him get a special ready as soon as possible."

"Yes, sir," said Pancoast, and he started away.

"And you, Miss Miles," turning to the head operating-room nurse, "I'd like you to get the emergency trunk out with all instruments, salt solution, other solutions, dressings, and anything else we might need. They didn't say whether there's a hospital there or not, so we'll proceed as if there weren't."

"Would you like me to go with you?" Miss Miles asked.

"Certainly would, and one other nurse. Thanks." As he disappeared into the doctor's dressing-room, Chuck was just coming out, dressed in white and ready to scrub up and take over the half-finished case.

With Dr. Finney out of hearing the operating-room began to hum with conversation only partially hushed and with the noise of nurses, doctors, and orderlies hurrying about gathering up the required paraphernalia for major operative work; but in the midst of it there was one man who sat unperturbed. He was the anæsthetist and if, in the excitement, others could give scant thought to the patient lying there unconscious on the table, his operation only half-finished, the anæsthetist was on the job. Old Griff, as everybody called him—Griffith Davis was his full name—had been at the game too long to be upset by anything, and more clearly than anyone else he realised the danger his patient ran in the prolonged anæsthesia that would be necessary. Without orders, therefore, he reduced the amount of ether he was giving to a quantity sufficient only to carry the young man along until adjustments could be made. And there he sat not saying a word, but confident that his charge was all right, until Chuck took over. The staff assistants had quietly kept the gaping wound covered with moist gauze.

When I heard that the Master was going to the wreck with a flock of assistants and nurses and on a special train, all thoughs of the Halsted band went out the window and I made up my mind to get on that train if possible. Man alive! Special train, flying lickety-split to a fearful wreck; excitement; adventure; unusual work; more excitement. I had never seen or experienced anything like that.

Going to the dressing-room I told Dr. Finney how distressed I was over the accident and then said: "Wouldn't you like me to get my new transfusion instrument and go up to the wreck with you?"

"Thanks, old man, but I don't think so."

"I'd be only too happy to go, and if a transfusion were needed I could do it."

"No, I think not. Thanks just the same."

Disconsolately, I went back to the operating-room and stood watching Chuck skilfully going on with the operation. There was no use asking Dr. Finney a second time; he was an easy-going man and always pleasant, but he never liked a fellow to be too persistent.

Chuck was getting along fine and was just about ready for application of the band when Dr. Finney came into the operating-room dressed and ready to go. Stepping up to the table, he said: "Chuck, I've decided to take you along after all. Suppose you drop out and let Bernie here," turning to me, "take over. But hurry up."

So luck was playing into my hands a little, anyhow, and I hurried out to change clothes and scrub up, delighted with the chance to try my skill on a human being. The whole business wouldn't take longer than ten or fifteen minutes, so perfectly had the preliminary preparation been done. Once I got going I had the band applied and was just in the act of tightening it up to the desired degree, perhaps the most important step of all, when back into the operating-room, all gowned and gloved again, came Chuck. An assistant standing at my right made way for him, but I was so intent on the work in hand that at first I didn't notice him.

"You're to drop out, Bernie," he said, "and I'll finish up. Dr. Finney wants you to go and get your new transfusion instrument as quickly as you can and meet them at the station. They've already left."

Was that a break! I hopped out of that operating-regalia and into my street clothes, and violated all speed laws getting to my office and grabbing the transfusion kit.

But I made the train—just. And what a train it was! Engine, baggage-car, one-day coach. I don't know what I'd envisaged, but it certainly wasn't that. A parlour-car, a sleeper, perhaps, a real train, glamorous, with officials aboard and porters all slicked up, train-men shouting, bells clanging, steam hissing, and engineers and firemen leaning out of cab windows receiving orders and shouting them —all panting to go. The very sight of that ordinary, bob-tailed thing, with that dirty coach, utterly deflated me. In addition to Dr. Finney, Pancoast, myself, and the two nurses, there were the conductor and brakeman—and nobody else. No excitement, no bells, nothing out of the ordinary. The conductor just casually came to where we were sitting, asked if that was the whole party, and, getting an affirmative answer, sauntered out and a moment or so later we left—just like any other train.

But that bob-tailed thing was no ordinary train. What it lacked in looks and style and railroad oomph it more than made up in fancy stepping, speed, slam-banging around curves, raucous whistle blowing. Right of way was what we had, and from the very start the engineer opened his throttle wide, hell-bent for his destination. Mile-long freight trains moved to sidings, great and important through passenger trains did likewise, and we could glimpse surprised passengers hanging out of windows as we sped by, screeching and howling, but never slowing down.

"Cripes! The guy's gonna kill us all," I yelled to Pancoast and was not reassured by his answer.

"Looks like it," he yelled back.

Miss Miles smiled a sickly smile. More than once she gave a little gasp as we hit a curve and went ricochetting round the bend.

Even the trainmen seemed uneasy and held on to the sides of their seats as we did. I couldn't laugh even when Miss Miles said she thought it was only Dr. Pancoast's extra weight that held us on the tracks. Dr. Finney was the calmest one among us, but he always was when up against it.

I never did see York, we flew through it so fast, and even when we reached Harrisburg, where I thought we'd surely slow down, that demon engineer went through, I would have sworn, with the wheels of only one side of his train on the tracks. Finally, we pulled right up to the wreck. It had occurred on a curve near a little nondescript station, and nearly the whole train had gone over the steep embankment. Fortunately, we were near a new and perfectly-appointed hospital that some wealthy woman had only recently built, and it was to this that the fifty or so injured and dying were taken, our particular patient among them. We found her in desperate shock and fearfully injured, chiefly about the face and head. It was touch and go for hours as we worked to save her, and only toward midnight was Dr. Finney sure she'd make it. I was glad he decided against transfusion; he wasn't sure of the intracranial condition.

By midnight, when she was coming round, the doctor thought I might offer my services to the other doctors who had been summoned. I did, and that was how I happened to witness a phenomenon entirely new to me then, but one that became more familiar later, on the battlefields of France. The wreck had occurred at about eight o'clock in the morning and some seven or eight negro men, cooks and waiters, had been in the diner kitchen as it rolled over the embankment. They, too, were taken to the hospital, all fearfully scalded, and when I was sent up to look them over some time after midnight, with a view to making them more comfortable, fixing their dressings and giving them water, I noticed that although they were quiet they were all wide-awake. Some were moaning; two or three breathed with a hissing sound that was new to me and very disturbing. With each intake of air they seemed to wince, as if in pain and their teeth chattered.

"Does it hurt you badly?" I said to one, sitting alongside his bed and taking his pulse, or trying to. It was running so fast I couldn't count it.

"N-n-no," he chattered back. "I'm—I'm cold."

He had two blankets around him, but I found another and was just putting it over him when suddenly he sat up, took two or three quick, short, sighing breaths, and dropped back—dead. I looked and found him scalded almost over his whole body; the skin hung in shreds.

I stayed in that smelly, stuffy, half-darkened ward till morning, working with the nurses and another doctor, trying to ease the sufferings of those men and giving such surgical aid as I could, for some of them were badly injured, in addition to being scalded. One more of them died suddenly as that first one died—right out of the clear, almost.

This was to prove a pre-view of the mustard-gas casualties of the first World War. There again, at a specially constructed place for study and observation of the worst mustard-gas cases, I saw men sputter and spew and suddenly die while you talked to them, their bodies burned all over and their lungs filled with the horrid stuff. We didn't know how to tide over the initial phase of the profound poison that was absorbed from the burned tissues or from inhalation.

That interrupted operation on the femoral aneurism* and certain other blood-vessel operations that later fell to my lot, plus the occasional appendix and hernia, were the extent of my surgical achievements before the first World War. With this sketchy experience behind me I don't need to confess that I was far from being an experienced surgeon when they signed me on with the Johns Hopkins Hospital Unit, but it was the only possible niche for me and I seized it. During those grim days at Belleau Wood and Chateau-Thierry, working in the front line, often with our own artillery pounding overhead, operating day and night, night and day, ceaselessly, interminably, where there were no specialists, no consultants, I learned more about surgery and gained more confidence than I could have in ten years of ordinary practise.

The war lifted me out of the near-surgeon class and, as a result, soon after my return to Baltimore I got a hospital service of my own which, through force of unusual circumstances, gave me an opportunity to make use of certain executive experience that had come to me during the war.

* The patient made a satisfactory recovery.

Interestingly enough, I had asked for a service in this very institution only a few years before the war, but had been told bluntly to "go out and get a reputation" and then maybe they'd consider me!

As the hospital required complete and fundamental re-organisation, the new job raised continually new, perplexing and aggravating problems. For the first time in my life I had to deal authoritatively with civilian doctors of all ages, grades and characters—not all staff members of the new clinic. And the fact that most of them freely admitted that they had to make a living and were going to do it, come hell or high water, was something new in my life. Not that the doctors I had previously known didn't also have livings to make, but they didn't talk about it, at any rate not so openly. In other words, there was a subtle but nonetheless definite difference in point of view between the two groups of men, and in charting my early course I failed to take the fact sufficiently into account.

For example, it had been the custom at the other hospitals at which I had practised to close down the operating-rooms to all but dire emergencies from twelve noon Saturday morning until Monday morning, the underlying idea being to give doctors, nurses, and operating-room personnel time off and to permit of fundamental cleaning. One of my first moves was to institute that procedure in my new post, and when objection was made I went to the mat over it and had my way. The doctors pointed out that their patients, being mostly of the middle-income group or lower, couldn't and wouldn't wait the two days and really counted on the week-end when they were not working. But they got nowhere with their arguments. I couldn't see it then. Later I came to realise that far from being closed down over week-ends, operating-rooms should really be in full swing on those days especially, and, for that matter, should never be closed to legitimate surgical procedures—daytime, night-time, Sundays, or holidays, not even the most solemn.

By the back door had I come into surgery, but by the front door had I come into a chief surgeon's job, and I was not entirely equal to it. To make matters worse, I was stubborn and up-stage. It never occurred to me that my erstwhile doctor friends might have been mistaken, that their ideas of the practice of medicine and the conduct of hospitals was reminiscent of a comfortable but fast disappearing era. Only gradually did it dawn on me that there are many different ways of life and that the man who aspires to leadership must have broad knowledge and sympathetic understanding. A man is not necessarily bad because he does things he oughtn't to. Many times he doesn't know any better. Sometimes he knows better, but through force of circumstances is unable to help himself. It is much easier for the man of means and secure position to have principles and to stick by them, than it is for one whose rent is overdue and whose wife and children are in want.

For a fellow who had most of the requisite qualifications for a chief surgeon's job—operating surgeon, teacher of surgery, administrator—it was startling to find myself so woefully weak on social relations, an element which, if the truth be known, had never entered into my calculations. Certainly I had no idea of its extreme importance or of the time and energy it took, the hundred and one things of an annoying nature that could constantly crop up and demand attention. Surgery was in my mind and operating; the task as I saw it then was making ward rounds and teaching young doctors how to diagnose and to operate. Yet there I was, harrassed to death half the time with things that irked my soul.

Take the one problem of abortions. I got a liberal education in that simply because the hospital, although it was a general hospital and by no means specialised in abortions, had been in the habit of admitting cases in quantity and no questions asked. I objected to the continuation of the practice on grounds that these cases took up too many beds to the exclusion of other types of major surgical cases without which you can't build up a surgical service or a resident staff. I made this point at ward rounds and privately, but got nowhere. The men said, and presumably with truth, that they didn't do the abortions themselves and, in fact, knew nothing about them until called, and "what was a hospital for, for God's sake, if not for hæmorrhaging women in danger of their lives?" There they were on solid ground, and I made it perfectly clear that it was far from my intention to refuse admittance to women seriously endangered, regardless of the cause. But they knew full well that the majority of abortion cases were in no such danger and if taken promptly could very well be handled in the home. I did add, because it was necessary, that if it became noised about that the hospital was no longer going to take abortion cases other than the extremely ill—of which the hospital authorities would be the judge—a decrease in applications might well follow.

I had quite a struggle over the whole matter and only won by theatening to keep a special list of those doctors who sent in or attended such cases, free or private, and to eliminate those who refused to co-operate. It was a hollow victory for me, because even then I was of the opinion that it was immoral to condemn women who didn't wish to go through with their pregnancy—whatever the reason—to the risks inherent in unorthodox abortion. If there had been any other way, if it hadn't been for the stigma attached to hospitals catering to abortions, if it had been possible to accomplish the real purpose for which I had come to the hospital and still keep taking the abortion cases, I'd have done so. But there wasn't. We didn't have the beds; and doctors of the better class, and patients, too, shy away from the institution with a questionable reputation.

If the medical profession had any guts it would long since have taken a stand in this matter and told society the truth. Indeed, I'm not so sure society would need much telling; for if the public were only partially informed, had the facts drummed into them day in and day out, if the thing were exposed in all its pathetic sordidness by high-grade publicists, with all its sufferings and misery and needless illness and death, I am optimist enough to believe there would be a change. Why can't we be as intelligent about abortions as we are about venereal diseases?

I didn't realise it at the time, but this episode was to prove a rich and extremely important experience to me. That whole period might well have been called "Bringing up the Chief Surgeon"; there were so many angles, not only to abortions but to many other problems, that I was amazed, even at times bewildered, at the things that didn't meet the eye in medical practise and procedure. They weren't illegitimate either, or not for the most part, and concerned chiefly money, rivalry, competition for practice, greed and hospital privileges. When I talked in after years with other hospital directors and chiefs of service I found they had not been plagued similarly and were far less *au courant* with the goings-on of doctors than I was. At first I couldn't understand it. It didn't occur to me that I had been talking almost exclusively to men who headed hospitals of the class where such problems really didn't exist, or not in the acute form.

When, having made this discovery, I sought out men who controlled hospitals similar to mine and had services in them, the story was quite different. They had learned how to deal with doctors and their problems on a practical basis, without frills or theory, and they, too, had found out, as I had, that their work wasn't by any means all operating, making ward rounds, teaching their young charges, attending medical meetings, and such. I liked them a great deal and though they had a far better, certainly more intimate, grasp of the real problems of medicine than the chiefs of the bigger and so-called better hospitals. I found, too, that generally they were more sympathetic and understanding and patient with doctors, young and old, and with the sick; and with the passing of the years I have become convinced that the higher-ups in medicine know too little at first-hand of the lower-downs and that therein lies much of the trouble—because it is the higher-ups who run the show.

B

3

SURGEONS AT A PRICE

THERE IS NO DENYING THE FACT THAT IT COSTS LIVES TO TRAIN and develop surgeons. Everything we do costs something. And there always has to be a first time—whether it's a baby's walking, or a man's taking out insurance, fighting, or operating—and firsts are usually shaky. So are seconds and often thirds: in fact until one gets the hang of things, insecurity and timidity must be one's portion and that is especially true of surgery. Teachers of surgery, supervisors, do their best to guide their charges' faltering steps, knowing well that human beings are the ones who must pay the penalty for mistakes; but there is much that cannot be reduced to absolute positive or negative much that must be sensed. It is impossible to know for a certainty when a young house officer is ready to handle the knife himself. There is no set time or rule; some boys just naturally "get it" while others don't. Some arrive early, others late, some not at all.

"Here Bob, you take the knife and open this abdomen," I said to my young assistant early one morning as we stood beside the table ready to begin—and I couldn't help smiling behind my face mask at the sudden, sharp look he gave me and his obvious confusion as he stammered:

"But——"

"You've got to begin some time, you know," I added, before he became too embarrassed, "and you are quite ready."

"You really think so, sir?"

"Yes, but don't let's talk about that now. You come on my side of the table and I'll switch over to yours, and let's go!"

I didn't hurry him exactly but I didn't let him loiter because it was imperative that he have no time to think it over. He was different from some of the others: timid, too cautious, too calculating and he had said that if it was all right with me he'd rather go slow. All the others wanted just the opposite. I couldn't quite make Bob out. I couldn't help feeling that maybe he was yellow and hadn't the guts, until one day a bit later on when the strangling baby came in. Without a moment's hesitation Bob grabbed a knife right out of the instrument cabinet and slit her windpipe open and saved her. That was something! He didn't wait to sterilise the knife or call for help or anything else. He just acted, and from that moment it was clear that in him we had a potential surgeon.

No two boys are alike, and the teacher who fails to take note of their differences gets nowhere. Environment, heredity, many factors enter the picture, and as far as possible I tried to study them. As chief surgeon it fell to my lot to choose the boys just out of medical school who were to become house officers on the surgical side. Since there were more applications than places and the applicants were from different schools, the choice wasn't always easy or simple. Whenever possible I liked to have the men come for a personal interview because you can't always judge a man by his record or by the marks he gets in school. Many boys are long on knowledge and book learning and short on common sense and general knowledge of people and the world they live in. You can't judge a man's personality, either, unless you see and talk to him.

And then there's the physical side; surgeons don't have to be six-footers and brawny, but they should possess energy and they should be healthy and strong, because their work with its long hours, irregular eating and sleeping, takes a great deal out of them. More than one man who did well as an interne had to be let out because he couldn't take it; to have kept him on as assistant resident in surgery would have meant too much of a gamble. Most of the men realised this fact, but the occasional one didn't and protested.

"Why don't you give me a chance?" said one who had his heart set on surgery and thought I was being unfair.

"If I had nobody else I would, but that isn't the case," I replied. "As between you and Tuttle there isn't much choice professionally, but there is physically."

"Couldn't I learn to take better care of myself?"

"Perhaps so."

"And isn't it fair to assume that in a year or two I might take on weight and get huskier?"

"Of course it's possible, but hardly probable unless you switch into some other branch. The records show that every time you were up all night somebody else had to do your morning's work. You couldn't do with an hour's rest like the others."

The boy argued fiercely and even got a mutual friend to intercede, but other staff men felt the same way I did, and the decision was made. That my judgment was vindicated by his coming down suddenly at a very early age with tuberculosis gave me no pleasure.

No one is infallible, and I made my share of mistakes in judgment. You can't tell how a fellow is going to do till he actually gets out on his own, and even then it takes time. One of my boys led me a dog's life and more than once I was on the point of letting him out—even as late as his last year—but each time some little thing came up that stayed my hand. Sometimes he was like a bull in a china shop and would get into bleeding that he should have avoided or tear into tissues in a manner to make one shudder, while the next time he'd do a beautiful operation.

"Look, Fred," I said to him once, "sponge your field clear of blood, like this, and try actually to see the bleeding point before putting on your clamp. Don't grab in the dark, because you might get hold of something you don't want, as you did with that common duct you had hold of yesterday when Dr. Lawson happened to walk into the operating-room."

"That was bad, wasn't it?" His frankness in admitting error was a little disarming.

"Sure was, and that's why I'm on the other side of the table to-day. You've been at the game too long for that and in six months you will be out on your own."

"But the cystic artery can be tough."

"Right, but that's no reason for your going off your head and failing to get it."

"Yes, sir. I'll try to do better."

"Well, let's see you get it this time, and with Frank here acting as your first."

He was a little surprised at that, because young Frank Ellsworth was only an interne. Nevertheless he was game, and as I swapped places and became second assistant it soon became apparent that he could do good work if he wanted to. It became equally apparent that young Frank knew how to handle himself, for he did measure up to his new job in masterly fashion. We gave him other opportunities later on and were pleased to note continued progress of a kind that assured him promotion at the end of his term.

There was another youngster, though, that I completely lost faith in. He had a lot of knowledge and when I or some staff member worked with him his work was good. Not spectacular, but good. I've often thought he might have got by if he hadn't been so undependable. I suppose you'd call it a moral blind spot, but he couldn't be made to conform. It was hard to make him out.

"Why didn't you wait till Dr. Green got here before going in on that case?" I said to him one morning after a particularly bad performance during the night.

"I did call him."

"But you didn't wait."

"He was held up or something, and the patient was bleeding, and I didn't think he could hold out." He always had an excuse, but this time it didn't work.

"You wouldn't think it was because you wanted to do a major case on your own and this was a good chance?"

"No, sir."

"Well, I do, and you will not become the resident." (He had been substituting.)

"But the patient is in good shape and—and——"

"And what?" I asked.

The boy was silent.

"We have rules and regulations at this hospital and they are specially specific and rigid about young, inexperienced surgeons like yourself taking matters into their own hands. You have a good mind and perhaps more than average surgical ability, but you seem to lack moral responsibility, and that makes you a menace to sick people who may be at your mercy. The fact that you apparently got by with last night's operation so far as life is concerned makes no difference whatever. If I can't depend on a man, I don't want him round me, and you fall in that category. Heretofore I have overlooked your delinquencies, thinking that they were due to youth and perhaps enthusiasm, but I find I was mistaken. I'd suggest that you take up some other and less exacting branch of medicine."

It is my guess that many a house officer who was not surgeon material kept his job for no other reason than that it was the easiest way out. No one likes to blast a young man's career, it doesn't do hospitals any good to let men out, and you're always saying to yourself: "He'll do better as time passes and he gets more experience. Besides, he's such a nice fellow." Before you know it the weakling has finished his residency, and yet another man who should never have become a surgeon is turned loose on an unsuspecting public, with heaven knows what consequences.

Although I tried to be utterly fair, I encountered some criticism for letting out the few men whose work I couldn't approve, but I always had the feeling that I wasn't nearly as ruthless as I should have been. Nor was it only my own bad judgment that permitted men to stay on after their interne year. Not every young doctor wants to be a surgeon, and not everyone who does want to can afford the long, hard grind of years before he makes even a pittance. Several times the men I chose wouldn't or couldn't stay on and those less desirable had to be accepted. There are many imponderables.

As long as department heads or their responsible assistants are present at operations, whether actually assisting or not, the costs of training surgeons are minimised. It's when they are not there or can't get there or, as so often happens, when they delegate authority over the telephone, usually at night, that the human costs rise. I have often thought that hospitals that take in accident or emergency work should have constantly in residence an experienced staff man, above and beyond the house officers. Not that he should do the work himself, but simply supervise it or be in the hospital in case.

How often have you read in the papers of people dying after being dragged into hospitals with gunshot wounds or stab wounds or other serious injuries? Those able to pay have the right to demand private doctors and, if conscious, often do—or their relatives do it for them. Sometimes they demand it even if they can't pay—and get it. If they are insurance cases, many hospitals will wait and get the insurance company doctors. But many victims are so badly injured that delay is dangerous. Besides, so often they are unassigned to any doctor. Occasionally two, three, or more are injured in the same accident.

In the better metropolitan hospitals resident surgeons are fairly well qualified to operate with or without supervision, but that is not so in too many other hospitals, metropolitan or not. Furthermore, some hospitals only keep their residents eighteen months, and I don't think a man of that degree of training ought to be permitted to do major operations without supervision. So you see how costs to patients can rise. You'd see still better if you took a look for yourself. Take, for instance, the case of some doctors who do industrial work. In one hospital they had the habit of turning over to the resident the operative cases they couldn't do, and paying him or giving him part of the fee. They were finally stopped, first because the resident in taking the fee was doing wrong, and second because the hospital authorities didn't think the resident himself was capable. Moreover, the authorities felt that if a doctor essayed to be a surgeon to an industrial or insurance company he should be qualified to do surgery. One of these men objected on the ground that most of his work was medical, whereupon it was suggested to him that he refer the surgical part to qualified surgeons. He did so, but only because the hospital refused him operating privileges.

It is my conviction that every major operation done in every hospital in the land ought to be recorded on a printed form in a special civic agency the day after it occurs, and that the character of the operation, anæsthetic, and operator's name, together with the operator's status or association with the hospital, should be clearly set forth. Results should follow. Especial attention should be given to accident and emergency cases, because these are the patients who, in the nature of things, have the least to say about their own handling. All records should be carefully scrutinised by responsible parties, so that men doing mediocre or poor work, whether residents or not, could be eliminated. In other words, society has certain rights, and one of them is to know exactly what is going on in hospitals. Society goes to considerable lengths to supervise its banks—even, indeed, to having the Federal Government insure funds deposited therein. Why shouldn't it go to similar lengths with regard to its hospitals? Is life of less importance than money?

4

IF I COULD CHOOSE AGAIN

IF I HAD MY LIFE TO LEAD OVER AGAIN AND IF I COULD KNOW medicines as I do now, I doubt if I'd go into private practise. I like full-time medicine: that is, I think I would prefer to be a salaried staff member of a medical institution —university, industrial, insurance, group, government— instead of a private practitioner working part-time on a hospital staff, and for the simple reason that I feel the institutional gentry have the best of it. True, they may not make as much money as some private practitioners do, but at that they don't do badly, and in any case they know where they stand from beginning to end. In sickness and during vacations their pay goes on; they do not have to kowtow to patients or bow to the whims or idiosyncrasies of other doctors; they do not have to run from house to house, hospital to hospital, in all kinds of weather; they are their own masters and, in a manner of speaking, the overlords of medicine—and they become more so each day. Most important of all, they have time to think.

Their freedom from the practical considerations that govern many practising doctors was illustrated recently by an example that came my way. The case was that of a pleasant-looking young married woman of twenty-four whose complaint was a goitre. She didn't look very sick and wasn't, but she had been nervous for several years and was getting worse. To just what extent her two children and the fact that her husband was in the Air Corps, though not overseas, affected the case we could not quite make out. She said they didn't, but we knew better or thought we did. The right side of her thyroid gland was definitely enlarged, but her pulse was not especially rapid and though there was a tremor to her hands it was felt that nothing acute was going on. Laboratory tests would, of course, give us more information, but they take time and so discussion waxed keen.

We were in the dispensary and I had my group of third-year students around me; in addition there was present a full-time staff man, considerably my junior in years, who had never been out in private practice. This doctor, who was one of the ablest of our surgeons, discussed that case from his standpoint and I discussed it from mine, with the students asking questions and obviously enjoying the show, as we did ourselves. For I think discussion of cases and problems between two or three staff men before students, with the students breaking in from time to time with their own questions and ideas, is one of the very best and most interesting ways of teaching.

There was no doubt of the enlarged thyroid (goitre), but the doctor felt that the case was more of a nervous imbalance than a toxic goitre requiring operation. He thought the basal metabolic rate, upon which we lay considerable emphasis, would be minus, whereas I thought it would be slightly plus; but in both instances that was of of course a guess and really not the point at the moment. The point was, should the patient have an operation now or not? The full-time man felt that she shouldn't. I couldn't quarrel with that from the institutional man's standpoint, but I remarked that generally the doctor on the outside would "do" that case immediately and without the slightest compunction.

"It is important for the students to know shades and highlights of pure hospital work versus private practice," I said, "and this is a case in point. My colleague here could say to this young lady: 'We don't think you need an operation now and maybe you won't at all. Maybe you are the nervous type, and while we do the usual tests, you just rest and do the things we tell you to do and come back for observation. Yours is a borderline case.'"

The doctor smiled and nodded his assent.

"That's good hospital medicine, but the doctor's livelihood isn't affected by it one way or the other. If a patient doesn't choose to take his advice and goes elsewhere it doesn't concern the full-time man in the least. But that isn't so on the outside where great rivalry exists and doctors earn their living by treating and handling patients, many of them with ills like this one, on the borderline. If one surgeon passed this case up, the chances are a hundred to one that she'd go to another surgeon who wouldn't. She has a goitre, she knows it, her physician sent her in, he probably thinks an operation is indicated; rightly or wrongly, he's the man who calls the tune, and an operation by someone it will be. Moreover, the surgeon who does it can rationalise the thing with perfect sincerity and honesty—and this, too, you who are young must know. People who have goitres that are of no consequence may go through life without any trouble whatever, but quite possibly they may not; and many men believe it is best to operate while the patient is quiet and in good shape."

"But suppose," said a student, "she *is* of the nervous type and it isn't the thyroid at all that's at fault."

"She still would get the operation on the outside because the doctors would insist that, tests or no tests, it's the thyroid that is back of the imbalance." They laughed and

I added: "There is some merit to that theory, but I'm giving you certain facts of life and they are not always the same in the eyes of the full-time men and of the private practitioners. The former can take the impersonal, objective view, but the latter can't—or think they can't, leastwise not always."

It is of the utmost important, I think, for young men who will one day take the field and doctor people to know life in the raw as well as in the pink. Whether we have private practice tomorrow on the same basis as today or whether we have great groups and insurance and the government takes a hand—with first-aid stations and hospitals, big and little, dotted throughout the land—it still will be necessary to deal with sick people in their homes and in the office.

For this one reason only, I might not have wanted to be a full-time man after all. Institutional work tends to narrow the doctor's horizon. He does not get about as other doctors do and he is not apt to know life, people nor the ways of men as he should—assuredly if he is to teach young men. I do not believe that doctors who have never doctored the poor, been in their homes, and done menial things, big and little and dirty and nasty, can "give" properly and adequately; therefore a sufficient number of men who have done yeoman work of this sort should be retained on teaching staffs. They should not be retained on sufferance, either, but as high-ranking, respected staff men, and under no circumstances should they be talked down to or told what they should not teach.

I think especially that there should be a much closer relationship than now exists between these clinical men and the men of science, because it so often happens that the practising men know the needs whereas the scientists who do not come in close personal contact with people who are ill cannot know them and the difficulties inherent in their ills. For this reason the full-time men are inclined to work chiefly on problems of scientific interest. I do not decry this tendency. Far from it, since very often their work leads or points to things practical; but at the same time the practical should not be neglected as it often is. At the same time I would encourage the practising man to do research himself if he can possibly get time, and I'd see that he got it if he had any problems. I'd give him all the help he needs, too, but would have him understand that he might not have sufficient knowledge of his own to carry his investigation through to the end.

That very thing once happened to me and a surgeon friend and it concerned the extremely important problem of intestinal obstruction, perhaps the most important and difficult problem, then and now, concerned with abdominal surgery. Being young practising men we met it ourselves with our own patients and came off second best. When we saw the same thing happen to other and better surgeons, we thought we'd have a try at it in the laboratory, and the authorities encouraged us. The full-time system was only then being inaugurated and there was more room in the laboratories then for part-time men.

My colleague and I did pretty well. We found out or clarified many things that weren't so clear before and we published our findings in order to stimulate other surgeons to attack the same problem. The condition was taking a much higher toll of life—usually following operation—than it should have, and something had to be done about it. We ourselves gave every spare hour we could to the work, and for two years, roughly, all went well. Then we came smack up against a phase that demanded scientific knowledge of a sort neither of us possessed—chemistry, pharmacology, bacteriology. Many things that look simple develop that way. We went to our books, but the going was bad. Such training as we'd had in school was minimal and had long since been forgotten in the business of becoming operating surgeons.

So we consulted the men of science and took our problems and our books to them, and though they were much occupied they were gracious and tried to teach us or at least guide our steps. But it was no go, and in the end we were compelled first to invite a scientist into the problem with us and then later to turn it over to him lock, stock, and barrel. At least I did. My colleague stuck by and the two overcame the thing that had held us back and went on to even greater endeavours. They did not solve entirely the problem of intestinal obstruction—indeed it still awaits complete solution—but that early work has not been dimmed by time.

I don't mind saying that it irked me to think that I had to give away a good problem because I hadn't the training and knowledge to carry it through; but it's a poor rule that doesn't work both ways: the scientific brethren sometimes have to come to the surgeons. For occasionally they come up against the same thing that we do, only in reverse. There was the colleague whose problem went all right as long as it was pure science, but lo and behold! his dogs had to have a bit of surgery if he was to go forward, and neither he nor his associates had the remotest idea how it should be done. The problem posed was a difficult one—and for me, too, when it was laid in my lap by my professor whom they had consulted; but by dint of a little experimenting and a certain amount of luck I solved it.

The problem concerned the liver. The scientific doctor

did his best to explain the details to me, but the more he talked the less I understood. Finally I said: "Just tell me, doctor, in words of one syllable what the surgical part of it is and what you want done. Maybe it can't be done, but we'll see." So we sat down over beer and cigarettes and he discarded his chemical and pharmaceutical formulæ and, in so far as possible, came down to brass tacks. Briefly, he wanted the circulation of the liver changed and while that had been done in the past—the so-called Eck fistula—the method was so clumsy and ineffectual that few could do it, and, to make matters worse, few of the animals lived long enough to be of real experimental value. And dogs were scarce!

It was an appealing problem from my standpoint and I devised a type of scissors that made the operation comparatively easy. The mortality was quite low, the dogs not only lived but seemed happy and content, and my scientific friends were delighted. The new method, scissors and all, was published, and scientists in other institutions were enabled to work on the same problem—and allied ones. For a year or so I personally did all the animals my friends needed, sometimes in their laboratory with their help, sometimes in the surgical laboratory with my own assistants; but later on, with the work getting heavier and the need for more Eck fistula dogs increasing, I taught them how to do the operation themselves and they became quite proficient—even though their surgical technique at times was on the sketchy side. Some years later another instrument—better than mine—was devised elsewhere and my operation was improved upon; but that was to be expected, and in any case you can see how even a curbstone surgeon can at times exercise a certain scientific influence.

Perhaps I might add that the scientists appreciated my efforts so highly that they tacked my name, along with theirs, on every article they published on that problem and that was quite a joke in itself because everyone knew I hadn't the remotest idea of what it was all about. If the operation had been feasible on the human being, we might have been able to help a number of liver conditions, but it wasn't. We made an investigation both on the cadaver and in the operating-room, but found that the structures in the human being differ in that regard from those of the dog and wouldn't permit the procedure. My friends of the laboratory felt as badly about that as I did because they knew how much success in the human being would have meant.

Without doubt it was my long and extremely pleasant association with scientists—I did other things of a surgical nature for them—and my observations of the life they led, the way they worked, and their great achievements (disappointments, too), that made me feel if I had to do it all over again I'd come close to casting my lot with them. Perhaps it is just as well that I shall not have to make that decision. To know people, to see life untrammelled and to take part in it is high adventure. The full-time hospital doctor, the scientist in his laboratory miss the passing parade and I cannot be certain I could endure that. Maybe that is why I squirmed out every time the scientists threatened to teach me their dreadful stuff. Maybe that's why to this day all I know is that in their lingo H_2O spells water.

5

BACK-DOOR SURGEONS AND
RESIDENT STAFFS

I HADN'T BEEN AT MY NEW JOB VERY LONG BEFORE IT BECAME apparent that I was to be plagued with back-door surgeons and would be obliged to do something about them. I never dreamed that there were so many men in Baltimore doing surgery who had had little or no training. When the problem began to unfold in my own hospital I quietly made inquiry elsewhere and discovered that the amount of surgery they were doing bulked large—up to one-half of all that was being done in the city at that time, and, according to some, even more. Hospitals like the one I became associated with were happy hunting-grounds of such surgeons because these hospitals were less well integrated, scantily endowed, and constantly in need of money; control passed from group to group in political fashion and almost anybody who had private patients was welcome. If that was the situation in Baltimore, one of the nation's great medical centres, I wondered what is was like elsewhere.

Few, if any, of the doctors I was compelled to deal with knew that I was a back-door surgeon myself, and I didn't tell them. It would only have caused trouble. Besides, there was really a big difference between them and me. Where I had aimed at surgery from the start and ate and slept surgery and studied it and watched good and bad surgeons do their stuff, day in and day out, at home and abroad, not occasionally or in haphazard fashion but year after year, and had ended up with war service, most of them had been—some still were—private practitioners of medicine who had somehow learned a bit of surgery and were doing what they could get. In other words, mine had been a long-time, comprehensive training and theirs definitely hadn't. Not all of these men were associated officially with the hospital. Many were merely men who had long been privileged to bring in private cases and operate on them as they wished, under supervision that was more perfunctory than real. Naturally not all the work was bad nor did people die right and left or suffer terrible things without dying. It is said: "You can get away with murder in surgery," and it is literally true because nature is so "grand". But there is another saying to the effect that "every surgeon has his own private bury-ing-ground", which, while it may reflect a modicum of truth, happily is not literally so.

Trouble came chiefly when the men in question took in too much territory surgically and did things they weren't qualified to do, or when something went wrong with the cases they were used to doing, like a hæmorrhage, follow-ing removal of tonsils or a trying bleeding during a hæmorrhoid operation. It was usually concerned with blood, and the men, not having had proper surgical train-ing, made a bad situation worse. Usually a resident doctor who "knew how" stepped into the breach and the day was saved. Sometimes a fellow who didn't exactly know how but wasn't afraid of blood was compelled to come to the rescue because nobody else was around.

Obstetricians who hadn't had surgical experience wanted to do pelvic work on their own patients, and some did— with questionable results. Men who called themselves general surgeons wanted to invade the specialist's field, and the occasional specialist thought he was qualified to do abdominal work. Tonsils and adenoids—well, they've always been jerked out pretty much regardless. It wasn't all bad but it was risky. For instance, take an ordinary appendix which can be the simplest and easiest of operations but also the most involved. You can never be sure what you're going to find. There may be other conditions that ought to be dealt with besides the appendix, and it isn't fair to the patient to pass them up because you aren't surgeon enough to do them—or to try to do them if you know you can't. But too often these men do try, and sometimes it is disastrous.

Some of these men, the best, were persuaded to visit certain of the nation's great clinics and take special courses in surgery. Several would have been glad to do so but couldn't afford to. They did, however, attend operations from time to time at the Hopkins, the University Hospital, and others of Baltimore's good hospitals. Others I tried to help as best I could, but for reasons of their own they didn't like that and it didn't work very well. Some of them I turned over to visiting men of quality—occasionally without their knowledge—and thus they received some instruction. It was a ticklish situation because you can't simply fire all men you think are not properly qualified to operate. Maybe you ought to—for the patient's sake—but I'm not so sure even of that. It would disrupt the service too much, maybe disrupt the whole hospital, and, if the truth be known, it wouldn't help the patients in any event. The doctors would only take them elsewhere, and there are always other hospitals that will gladly accept these doctors and accord operative privileges. Moreover, the patients themselves would nearly always stand by their doctors; they never would fully understand why their doctors had been turned away and wouldn't believe anything ill against them no matter who said it. So they would follow them wherever they went, pay good money to these ill-equipped men, and let them operate even to the death. There is so much to medicine that the ordinary layman doesn't know and can't understand.

I did, however, insist that all surgeons stick rigidly to their fields and permitted some to operate only under supervision. Physicians who were in the habit of operating were gradually eliminated and obstetricians without surgical training for abdominal work were not permitted to perform such work. The man who refused to conform was deprived of all operative privileges temporarily or, in a very few cases, for good. There was much criticism and for a time it looked as if the new regime wouldn't last; but as the wisdom of the steps taken and the emphasis on the patients' welfare became apparent, the gale was weathered.

It was inevitable that this new and diverting experience should affect my thinking. I wrote an article called "The Unknown Surgical Mortality" and presented it in good faith before the American Medical Association then meeting in Atlantic City. But when it came to publication the Association refused to let it appear in the *Journal*. They preferred to bury it in the archives because they thought it would do more harm than good. Perhaps they were right, but there was no question then, and I don't think there is much now, that there are many surgical deaths and bad results about which no one ever hears. Top-ranking surgeons do the least of the nation's operating, but it is their work and their results chiefly that you read about. I didn't realise this until I went back-stage and had it brought home that the little fellow you don't know and never hear about is extremely active; he says nothing, publishes nothing, good or bad, but perpetrates much.

Before writing the article, I had taken the trouble to look about me wherever I went and had discovered that this state of affairs not only existed locally but was quite common throughout the nation.

Fortunately, the problem is not as bad now as it was then, but only recently an insurance company asked me to appear as an expert witness for them in the following case. A man in his early forties dropped a piece of wood on the toes of one foot, a bruise resulted, it didn't heal, and eventually the insurance doctors discovered he had peripheral vascular disease, diagnosed first as Buerger's disease but later as Raynaud's, the two being somewhat similar. The company paid the man and treated him, but he wasn't satisfied and of his own accord went to a hospital where he was subjected to a special nerve operation by a surgeon who, the company agent said, was doing it for the first time—and the man died. Thereupon his family wanted the complete indemnity of some five thousand dollars, not, as I understood it, because he died as a result of the operation, but because his disease was aggravated by the accident so that he had to undergo an operation which otherwise would not have occurred!

Of course there always has to be a first time for everything, surgery included; but in the hands of the properly qualified the operation in question has had a low mortality, so far as we know.

I refused the invitation because I don't like to go before courts. Too much time is lost, lawyers always try to make a monkey out of doctors and altogether it is unsatisfactory, or most doctors think it is. Most doctors think medical men should come into court only as "friends of the court", and I subscribe to that.

All hospitals are supposed to study their mortality and

other records, and no doubt they do, but it's so easy to cover up. If you do an appendectomy and the patient gets a post-operative pneumonia and dies, how are you going to record it? Or if you operate on an accident case in shock, with or without a transfusion, and the patient promptly dies, how are you going to record that? Surgeons have ways and means of meeting such situations. I once sat in on a conference and heard a surgeon who had committed a grave technical error during the course of an operation go to the mat with his chief, saying that the resultant obstruction had been relieved before death, that the records should show embolus and nothing more. Even when one has no wish to cover up, it isn't always easy. For example, how about cases that die immediately after leaving the hospital or after a week or two? Some doctors have a habit of getting certain cases out quickly! I personally counted every death that followed operation *in the hospital* as a surgical death, regardless of terminal things like pneumonia and embolus. Some of the men didn't like it even though they had to admit that the patients wouldn't have developed pneumonia or embolus or other complications if they hadn't been operated on.

The whole business of surgery as I saw it revealed— mortality, suffering, fees, emergencies done at night and at other odd hours, doctors going out of their own orbits, fee-splitting, errors in judgment—convinced me that surgeons, of all men in medicine, should *not* engage in private practice. I shall not discuss the matter here because I wish to go into it in some detail later on, but as the years progressed I became more than ever convinced that no man ought to make personal gain out of operating. It is too important, is loaded with dynamite; being human, a surgeon might find his judgment swayed by the fact that he will get considerable money if he does operate—and little or none if he doesn't. Not all men are above monetary and other mundane considerations, and you never know when a man is under pressure or how it will affect him.

But the back-door men weren't the only problem. When we got on our feet and put up a handsomely equipped new building, we ran head-on into a problem exactly the opposite. Before long, well-established surgeons from other hospitals began to send us some of their private patients. This in itself was good. However, I suspected that they were bringing certain of their wealthier clientele to us in order to evade the thousand-dollar ceiling for private operations in their own hospitals. In the first place, that was none of my business, and, in the second place, I didn't blame them.

When a hospital admits private patients to special, semi-private or even wholly private pavilions at cost or lower—as is the case in a number of places—and when it limits the patients occupying such accommodations to those of the lower-income brackets—up to twenty-five hundred or three thousand dollars—I think it has the right to ask and even insist that doctors put a top limit of, say, a hundred and fifty or two hundred dollars on their charges. When, however, patients are admitted who pay the full rates—whether they can afford them or not—and ask no questions or favours, it seems to me that it is rank interference with a doctor's private business for any hospital to say what he shall or shall not charge for his services. It is a well-known fact that a one hundred or two hundred dollar charge works a greater hardship and is relatively far higher to some patients occupying private rooms than a charge of a thousand dollars or more is to the patient who may be in the next room.

I dare say hospitals that have ceiling rates do so because they do not want it said that patients coming into their private wards are being mulcted, whether they are or aren't; but even that is no excuse and is a pernicious interference with a doctor's private rights. You either have private practice or you haven't; and in any case it is not the business of the hospital's directorate to regulate the matter— certainly not without the doctor's consent.

But this is beside the point. We would have welcomed these new surgeons if they hadn't insisted upon ignoring the rule about our resident staff. They conformed quite willingly to the rules in their own hospital but not in ours, giving as their reason the inexperience of our internes and residents.

"Then I'll send my men to your clinic," I said to one prominent man, "and you can train them to your liking."

"But that takes time and energy, and I'd rather bring my own assistant. Don't be childish."

"I'm not being childish, doctor. You can't have one rule for one man and another for another. If you bring in your personal assistant, other surgeons will demand the same right, and before long my residents will all be leaving."

They would have been right in doing so. You can't expect a young doctor to hang on when he sees that he is losing the chance for which he has slaved three long years, simply because the surgeon prefers to work with his own assistant. No hospital can build a competent resident staff under such conditions, so I made a point of the inviolability of the resident staff from the first moment of my incumbency.

"One of the troubles with this hospital," I once said to the gathered surgical staff, old and young, "has been an utter lack of appreciation and consideration of the internes. You can't attract good men unless you take pains to teach them, unless you promote them in logical order, year in and year out, for work well done, and unless you see that they are given absolute protection. And by that I mean no taking in of men from the outside and jumping them over your own men for advanced standing, and no bringing in of a doctor's own personal assistant to help him, over the resident. And that goes regardless of the speciality. The resident surgeons will be first and second assistants at all operations—mine as well as yours—but if it turns out that they aren't as skilled as they should be in brain work or other specialties, we will allocate one or the other for special intensive instruction in that branch. We will not permit an outside assistant to come in. To do that would destroy morale and would make it impossible to develop and hold the good resident staff which, you all realise, is the backbone of a modern hospital."

With the surgeon who accused me of being childish, and with others, I made my point and stuck to it. But in another instance I came mighty near to defeat and learned a great deal about certain aspects of hospital management of which I had been happily unaware.

One doctor who had never before operated at my new hospital brought in several patients over a period of a couple of weeks and told me things had gone very well in the operating-room. Then, one morning, he brought along his own personal assistant and very pleasantly but definitely made the hospital's resident play second fiddle. After the operation he put his arm about the young resident's shoulders and in his most charming manner said: "You won't mind if I bring Johnson in to help me, will you? He's had so much experience, and it makes things go a lot easier for me."

The youngster had the good sense to make no reply.

"Johnson will come around to see my patients from time to time, too, and together we'll give you a lot of pointers."

The surgeon was gracious and very appealing, but he had encountered a young man who knew his rights and meant to have them. Within an hour he laid the matter in my lap and before the day was out the whole hospital was agog. That doesn't take much, it is true, since hospitals are veritable beehives of intrigue and gossip, but in the present instance it was as if an earthquake had rocked the place.

There I was, being defeated by a surgeon who should have known better. In an interview in his own office I had it out with him and was amazed that he couldn't see a thing wrong in his actions.

"You must take into your calculations what it means to a hospital to have me work in it," he said.

"I most certainly do, but——"

"And you mustn't be small-minded and look upon me as just another doctor."

"Quite true, but——"

"Your residents are rather good but, naturally, they can't know the finer points of my work." He wouldn't let me get a word in. "And I can't get along without able assistants."

"But granting everything you say," I finally broke in, "if you have that privilege others will want it—and insist on having it."

"Not if you explain it to them properly."

"The trouble is that while my residents recognise your pre-eminence they refuse to play second fiddle in their own hospital."

"I refuse to believe it."

"It is true, nevertheless. Their idea is to let the big shot strut his stuff in his own back yard and no offence taken, but don't let him come into ours and try to do the same thing, because we won't stand for it."

It had become necessary to give it to the surgeon straight, regardless of consequences. I had been advised to ask an older colleague to see him and straighten things out, but had demurred on the ground that a man either did his job or didn't, and in my own case I wasn't going to have one rule for the little fellows and another for the prima donnas. I did my best in the present instance, even going so far as to offer to send an assistant resident to the doctor's own clinic for special training and to assign him as personal assistant; but I got nowhere. The doctor was good-natured and pleasant enough, but insisted that I was making a mountain out of a mole-hill. Moreover, he was accustomed to getting his own way. When I told him that long months before he brought in his personal assistant, other surgeons had tried it and been properly set down, he said he thought that a mistake had been made and that maybe if I had consulted my board they would have advised me to take a different course.

"But what has the board got to do with the rules and regulations of a surgical clinic?"

"Nothing theoretically but plenty practically."

"I don't get it."

"Bernheim," he said, "you're too naïve for words." And no sooner were the words out of his mouth when a great light shone in my brain and I knew he was right. I had been dumb, stupid, and the realisation made me blind with anger—anger at myself and anger with this eminent surgeon who was acting pettily and improperly, yet withal unwittingly doing me a much-needed service. He didn't need to tell me in so many words that the lay board of my hospital were more than pleased at his growing activities there and that since they were concerned with finding the money required to run the place I had best keep them much in mind in any decision I might make with regard to him. It was an unfair advantage and I guess he wouldn't have taken it if he hadn't seen that I was bent on making him conform.

I learned more during that interview than I realised at the moment, and the least of it was medicine and surgery. I think the doctor learned something, too, because he was much upset by the time I took leave and just a bit apologetic.

"If what you say or hint with regard to hospital boards is true," I remarked, "and if the man they appoint to head one of their big clinics has to kow-tow to them in matters that he regards as purely professional and therefore in his own domain, then to hell with them and their whole god-damned hospital. I don't want any part of it."

"Wait a minute. You mustn't go off half-cocked," he interposed.

"I'm not. I'm merely stating a fact."

"But people must learn to live with each other, and a hospital is composed of a lot of parts. You must see that."

"Indeed yes, but a man must have his principles."

"They can be elastic."

"Well, sir," I said finally, "it may not be right for a small-time guy like me to say to a man of your professional eminence that I will not permit you to bring your personal assistant into my clinic again, but if you do, I shall hand in my resignation to the board that very minute. We shall see then just what they think is most important in the run-ning of a hospital and in the building of a clinic that has been shot to hell for years and is only now showing signs of life."

The doctor had given me the out himself—and knew it. He never operated at the hospital again as long as I was associated with it. Outwardly he was friendly, but I don't believe he ever fully forgave me. The board? They asked no questions—of me. Rumour had it that they asked plenty of others.

6

LEARNING THE JOB

TO UNDERSTAND WHY I WAS SO FIERCE ABOUT THE RIGHTS OF my young residents, you must know that surgery cannot be learned in textbooks. It must be learned by watching and doing, and the teaching is individual. For instance, my first assistant and I, gowned, gloved, and masked, are about to open an abdomen. That is, I do the opening and he does the assisting. This is the way he learns the art of making his fingers think and see and grow as nimble as the digits of Jascha Heifetz. Unlike Lionel Barrymore's Doctor Gillespie, a surgeon does not pull his diagnosis out of the air.

A long smooth cut is made, laying open the skin of the patient's upper right abdomen. Although the case has been studied, it is not entirely clear, and this is an exploratory operation, the final diagnosis to be made as we go along.

"What'd you say that the lady's chief complaint was?" I thought it wise to rehearse the salient features of the case.

"Indigestion, burning pain after eating, nausea."

"Catch that vessel," I interrupt, "and wipe a little faster, so I can see." Then: "Indigestion, pain. Any vomiting or blood?"

"Yes, sir. Once or twice. No blood."

"Jaundice?" I separate the muscle fibres and plump down on the peritoneum.

"No, sir."

"Here, catch that edge." I nick the peritoneum. "Guess the woman's been quite a sufferer—or is it mostly in her head?" enlarging the incision. "Looks all right so far, but we'll soon know. There's the gall bladder poking up. Doesn't look too bad, but"—and here I gently slip my gloved right hand into the abdomen—"I think I'll take a feel all around first." Assistants, nurses, all stand quietly, doing nothing as this goes on—a man, myself, seemingly looking into space, hand in the patient's abdomen half-way up to the elbow, carrying on a monologue aimed at nobody in particular. "Gall bladder's tense and wall's thicker than usual, but I can feel a number of stones. Adherent to surrounding structures. Dense. Nothing in stomach, but we'll take a look at that later." I stop talking momentarily and swish my hand slowly, gently down towards the right side. "Appendix seems bound down a bit. Right ovary O.K., not enlarged. Left ovary's got a little cyst attached to it." For a moment I explore further. "Both kidneys seem all right, and so's the spleen. Head of the pancreas not hard."

I withdraw my hand. "Let's take a good look at the stomach," I remark, and shove my hand back in, but towards the upper left, and feel around a bit, and then slowly withdraw it, bringing along the body of the stomach itself.

"Take hold, John"—as John, first assistant, substitutes his hand for mine—"and don't let it get away. Looks all right at the pylorus. No ulcers. No growth. But what's this?" I feel along the organ's upper edge and gradually deliver more of it up into view. "A little induration and, yes, I think I can feel the scar of an old healed ulcer. Here, let me hold that and you slide your fingers in there. Feel it?"

"Yes, sir."

"Be sure, now. Describe it."

"Indurated area about an inch in diameter, up high on lesser curvature."

"That's right. Question is: Is that all and is it entirely healed? These things fool you sometimes. How old is she?"

"Fifty-eight, sir, and not very robust."

"Humph. I'd like to look inside that stomach, but guess we'd better give her the benefit of the doubt and just take out the appendix and gall-bladder." And at once I begin to mobilise the appendix.

Or, as so often happens, the operation is not exploratory but an emergency in the dead of night. It's that way far too often, and as I step up to the table I can detect grins even through the gauze face masks of nurses and doctors. "Give me a knife now," I usually mumble, "and let's get through this little affair. Gosh, I did hate to get out of bed."

As the incision is made, my assistants bend to clamp bleeding vessels and wipe blood out of the deepening wound.

"Nothing like a McBurney incision for these things, and muscles of kids like this are thin and delicate, easy to separate."

The team is clicking, all hands working smoothly, as if directed by one brain; no one getting in the way of anyone else. Not so simple as it sounds.

"Old Ben [Dr. Crocker] says the child's been sick two days, but they only called him a couple of hours ago. Usual stuff. Put a small retractor in there and another in here. That's it. Now pick up the peritoneum opposite me. Fine."

Carefully nicking the filmy tissue with the sharp edge of my knife, I note the cloudy fluid, possibly full of strep infection, that wells up. I make the opening larger, shift the retractors inside the abdomen, and then carefully, gently, proceed to feel for the appendix.

"Got to go easy in cases like this. I couldn't feel a mass on examination at the home, but the child looked sick; and with temperature, pulse, and leucocytes so high, the appendix is certainly gangrenous, if not ruptured."

Assistants stand by quietly, clamps and gauze in hands, ready for action.

"I feel it; rather tense, adherent, twice normal thickness. Give me a long forceps and a small, moist strip." I withdraw my fingers and prepare to wall off the surrounding gut.

"Think she's busted?" asks the first, deftly placing one end of the sponge down toward the wound, which I widen just a bit to facilitate movements.

"No, but if I'm not careful she will be. Let's have another strip. There. That's it. See her down there?"

"Yes, sir."

"Take a feel," and the first slips the two first fingers of his left hand in.

"You left-handed?"

"No, sir. Why do you ask?"

"Well, it's a funny thing about the sense of touch. Go easy, now, and for Pete's sake don't——"

The first's hand is out before I finish.

Without further ado I slip my own left forefinger down into the wound and work smoothly, deliberately, every once in a while taking a look, now coming completely out and having the first sponge and the second shift his retractor to get more exposure. In short order we have an

ominous-looking, markedly swollen, cyanotic, but un-
ruptured appendix exposed and freed for removal.

Nothing is said, except the usual soft-spoken demands
for ties, needles and thread, scissors and clamps, until, the
tension obviously released, I become a teacher again.

"About that sense of touch, now . . . Here, nurse, give
me a continuous suture for the peritoneum . . . Most
surgeons find that their sense of touch is not the same in
both hands, and when they are up against it and want the
utmost delicacy of manipulation, when they desire the nth
power of knowledge from feeling, they invariably use the
one hand . . . Now for a few interrupteds . . . That's
fine . . . And strangely enough, the occasional one like
myself, and maybe John—the fellow who does everything
right-handed—relies most on his left . . . Ever notice it,
John?"

"No, sir. Only now that you mention it, I guess——"

"Would you mind sewing up the skin? Thanks. That's
one that's better out than in, and that little excess of
exudate we noticed is hardly of any consequence. Give him
plenty of fluids, no food, and sedatives as needed."

Since it is night and I have been working all day, I feel
close to exhaustion and very much relieved that the emergency operation has gone off without a hitch. I even hum
a little as I step away from the table while the nurse unties
the strings holding my mask and gown. I slip off rubber
gloves and other paraphernalia, nod to my assistants, and
head straight for bed.

It has been my job and that of my staff to give the
graduate M.D.'s who are trying to become surgeons a
chance to explore the insides of my patients, public and
private. On an ordinary day I may perform several such
operations, and by the time my assistants have watched

and taken part in a few—twenty-five, fifty, perhaps a hundred—they begin to get the hang of things. If the time ever comes when you have to call in a surgeon and you call one who has come in through the front door, you'll be comforted to know that he has spent long years of apprenticeship and has seen and done, again and again, almost everything in the surgical category.

We surgeons who teach doctors to become surgeons lead them by the hand—and I mean that literally. I sometimes actually take my assistant's hand and guide it down to the unseen pathological structures. I want to get him to the point where, by touching the tissue as I do, he can arrive at the same conclusion. I try to develop in him the faculty of diagnosing through his finger-tips, even though his hand at the moment may be out of sight. He doesn't reach me for instruction until he has mastered any number of beautifully illustrated six-inch-thick volumes on surgery, complete with footnotes; but we do not learn how to operate from text-books. I studied pathology before I studied surgery in order to learn what to look for. Young John M.D. will watch and assist, and watch and assist—from the other side of the table—long months before he touches a patient with a knife. His first step in surgery is tying off small blood vessels, and that is important because tying knots is an art in itself. Only when he becomes my first assistant—much, much later—does he assume a responsible part in the team.

When your surgeon operates on you, he doesn't work alone; he works as quarter-back, calling the signals to his surgical team. Your surgeon performs the operation, but the first assistant can make it a good or a poor one. If he is clumsy, his hands will get in the way of the operator; in trying to be helpful, he will only hinder. I can usually spot an up-and-coming surgeon by how good he is as first assistant.

With a smoothly working team, in the case of an operation that doesn't develop a sudden hitch, actions are almost automatic and reflex. The surgeon and assistants can perform a competent job and yet be talking at the same time—and not always of the case in hand. Every operation is also a demonstration, and since there are always some kibitzers—students, staff members, visiting physicians and surgeons, sometimes as numerous as at a pinochle game—during a lull in the action some of them, properly gowned and masked, may even be invited to step up to the operating table for a close-up, intimate view of structures and operative steps.

There comes a time in many operations—usually along toward the end, after the main steps have been taken and the tension has been relieved and only the so-called closure remains—when surgeons, assistants, and sometimes nurses and onlookers begin a running conversation. It was on one of these occasions when I was watching Professor Halsted operate that the professor and his first seemed especially engrossed, and though they had much to say to each other, it was all *sotto voce,* and no one else heard a word. The entire audience was desperately interested, as it always was in anything the professor had to say. I felt he was discussing some fine points that he didn't want us to hear, and was slightly picqued.

Later I waylaid the resident and asked him what in the world the conversation was about and why the secrecy.

"Did you see Strangler Lewis wrestle last night?" he asked.

"Yes, I was there."

"Well, the professor was there, too. He thinks Lewis is a

darn good wrestler, but he didn't like the way he was using the toe hold. He was discussing the toe hold and the ethics of using the toe hold all the time."

But don't worry—the surgeon takes it easy only when everything is under control. Let something go wrong, a sudden emergency, an unexpected slip—a hæmorrhage resulting from a broken thread—and, in a flash, hands that were moving slowly and deliberately in normal fashion take on almost blinding speed; rhythm gives way to the jerky motions needed to grasp new and different instruments hastily handed them. At every operation we have ready and waiting many more instruments than needed—just in case. The running conversation ceases; the nurses and orderlies stand hushed and tense. At such times, one man, and one man only, speaks. His words are sharp and staccato, but his voice is never raised. He is master of himself and the situation, and it is the surgon who, with all the responsibility, still steadies the rest of the team.

The moment the emergency has been dealt with successfully, you can practically hear the relaxation of tension, and once again normal conversation is resumed.

"Ligature slipped over the end of that vessel down there," said my own chief, after a well-remembered episode, "and that's a good lesson for you fellows. The only man who has no accidents is the one who does no operating. I preach and shall continue to preach that every effort should be made to keep out of trouble, for the simple reason that it is easier to keep out than to get out after you have once got in. This is a lesson in point, and since the patient might have died then and there, I doubt if any of you will forget it."

He was right. And that's one way your surgeon learns—by emergencies.

The better hospitals work on a process of rigid elimination. A graduate M.D. who aspires to surgery goes through four stages—interne, second assistant, first assistant, and resident. His surgical work takes four years in addition to his regular four years in the medical school. Let us say that a given hospital has twenty internes. Out of these we may select two or three to remain on for an additional year as second assistants, and when that year is completed the one or two best of the three are kept on a third year as first assistants, with the fourth and final year going to the one who appears to be most apt. This man becomes the resident surgeon, so called, and is taught actual operating. In larger hospitals, there may be two or more such residents, one for each service.

These men are good and they have a hard row to hoe. We have to be tough. We eliminate many good men, and sometimes make glaring mistakes. I remember one aspirant. We all thought he was good, and so did he, until one day an emergency arose, and he did an operation on his own without the direct supervision of his chief, a most unusual occurrence. At that, he might have got by if a junior staff man hadn't happened to wander into the operating-room and notice the excessive bleeding the patient was having.

"If the youngster had only been sweating, I wouldn't have thought so much of it," the doctor reported.

He almost had us fooled. But when the chips were down, he couldn't come through. He didn't act—or react—like a surgeon. At the end of an operation, even a minor operation, most surgeons are drenched with sweat, from inner tension. The operator who doesn't sweat over a job, especially when he gets into trouble, generally hasn't got it in him to be a surgeon.

Before a doctor can call himself a surgeon, his every move is watched, and, knowing that, the mental and emotional stress during the long years of his training builds up as surely as Eisenhower's did before D-Day. If he is a clumsy assistant and breaks technique oftener than he should or tires too easily, if he gets unduly nervous during the minor operations first allotted to him and has trouble making up his mind what he should do in the accident rooms, he is hardly the man we want. You can't make false starts in surgery and repeat, and indecision is fatal. A good surgeon must have enough confidence in himself to get dangerously close to a major artery without acquiring a case of the shakes, and if he gets nervous in the face of that or any other danger, he hasn't got what it takes. All the brilliant technique in the world and all the knowledge are worthless if he can't handle himself at the critical moment.

We who teach young men to become surgeons lead them slowly, gradually, carefully, inculcating in them gentleness and respect for tissues and the need for conserving blood. In an efficient operation there is very little bleeding; this is accomplished by a system of applying clamps—sometimes there may be two dozen or even more in a wound. The assistants do this as the surgeon cuts, and later on these clamps are removed by tying with silk or catgut the little points they hold. This sounds very simple, and it is—to the one who knows how to tie knots. I practised the art hours and hours, using up miles of light and heavy thread on the arms of chairs.

In the critical operation, especially if the blood vessel lies deep, most surgeons tie their own knots. The old-fashioned granny knot is the stand-by and is usually tied triple, but the art comes in tying the second knot, because that is the one that most often breaks. We go to great lengths teaching asistants to tie good knots, because if one slips or breaks after the clamp has been removed, a serious hæmorrhage may occur before the clamp can be reapplied.

One young surgeon learned a valuable lesson through the recurrence of a hernia before the patient got off the operating table. The young operator had done the operation very well, and the nurse in charge told me she had never seen a hernia job done more smoothly. But in his enthusiasm to do an especially fine job, the operator tied fancy knots and had the anæsthetic discontinued a little too early; the patient began to wake up, gave a little cough —then a bigger one—and there, larger than life, was the tell-tale swelling in the groin, just as it had been before. The knots had not held.

The staff surgeon sent in to take over made the youngster open up the wound and clean out the bits of thread that lay loose in it. Then, using the old reliable granny knots, he did the usual repair—and one young man learned a valuable lesson, while the patient suffered no other harm than spending a little extra time on the table. A half-dozen visiting experts witnessed the episode, and that was good, too, because a man, especially a surgeon, has to learn how to take it and like it.

After a young man has proved himself by assisting in a variety of operations and seems ready to handle the knife himself, we select a few simple cases of the "less major" type and, instead of his assisting us, we assist him. In this manner the welfare of the patient is secured and the young operator is given the confidence needed, for it is one thing to assist, quite another to operate. We guide him and, experienced in teaching, lead him to think he is making all the decisions and doing all the work. It is a trying time

c*

68 <small>A SURGEON'S DOMAIN</small>

and many a man is made or broken at that point.

For then comes the question of judgment, which some men have and others do not. It may be acquired, and we go to great lengths to give it to our protégés; but, unlike giving them nimble fingers and good technique and teaching them how to dissect and sew, we have our troubles with this elusive element which, in the last analysis, is something personal and definitely "of the mind". All the best surgeons have it highly developed, and in great measure we grade our young surgeons by the degree of their sound judgment, knowing well that experience and much hard work on their own will play a great role in their getting it or not.

Once the budding surgeon gets hold of himself, we, the teachers, drop out of his operations and let one of his confreres take our place as assistant. This puts him on his own, but it does not mean that we give him free rein. To do so would be unjust to the patient, and so we stand by and watch or perhaps go to the doctors' room for a smoke. This all makes for confidence, and as time passes and operations succeed operations—with the major succeeding the relatively minor—we give the impression that all supervision is off, while having a younger staff man wander in occasionally and seemingly accidentally, and slowly, gradually note and take pride in the development of yet another surgeon who can be trusted.

At that, though, the new brother isn't a finished product, and nobody knows it better than himself. It is results that count in surgery, as in all things, and so, as our protégé begins to operate, we scan his cases with an eagle eye to see how well they do after operation, whether they have smooth or stormy convalescence, whether their wounds heal as they should or become infected, whether they are cured of the affection for which they have been operated on or are benefitted as much as they should be. In short, there is a balance sheet, but in its review we recognise again that the only man who gets no bad results or has no deaths is the one who does no operations.

Surgeons are without question the worst patients in the world. Better than anyone else, the surgeons knows what it means to be operated on. Let him get an ache or a pain, let him develop a gall blader, a hernia, an appendix, and watch him doctor himself and keep his ailment a deep secret even from his wife and family. The only time he takes his own medicine is when he is so ill he knows the jig's up. Then he gets panicky. There's the little matter of pain and distention and other minor tortures. Looming importantly are the rarer complications that surgeons know best, the signs of which haunt them day and night until they become nervous wrecks.

Surgeons, the last people to take their own medicine, often josh each other about the fact, reciting their various ailments, together with remedies wondrous and bizarre, Never, though, have I been more amused than when I saw one of America's well-known wielders of the knife stop in the midst of removing two-thirds of a man's stomach because of ulcers and receive a glass of milk, through a tube proffered by a nurse, for his own ulcer.

7

IN THE DISPENSARY

TO BE A GOOD DISPENSARY SURGEON YOU'VE GOT TO HAVE A
sense of humour and you must know your stuff, but above
all you must realise that most of those who frequent
hospital dispensaries are self-respecting people who are
down on their luck, and not bums. Whites and blacks,
Italians, Greeks, Russians, it matters not who they are or
where they come from, they're all sick, or think they are;
they all have problems, and if you're going to do them any
good, it's up to you to win their confidence by whatever
means you can and get the story behind the story.

One morning as I came on duty—it was my job to see
that all patients received attention and, in addition, to
instruct a group of third-year students—they were having
a terrible time in one of the booths. I thought it wise to
look in.

"It's like a poppa he iss to you!" shrieked Mrs. Gold-
berg.

"Open up, buddy, open up!" demanded the young
interne for the fourth or fifth time.

"I wanna go home!"

"Poppas don't hurt!"

"Yah-h! Yah-h!" bawled little Jakie, louder than ever.

"Why not take a peek at his throat while he's howling,
doctor?" I ventured.

"Why—why——"

"Just a trick of the trade, you know, but well worth knowing."

But little Jakie was tough and though he kept on yowling, the young doctor couldn't get the look he wanted. That angered him. It angered the mother, too, so she decided to help matters by giving her seven-year-old a smack on his mouth, which only made a bad situation worse. It always does. It's also a bad thing for a doctor to lose his temper.

"Come here, you!" the stalwart doctor said. Grabbing the boy he tried to hold the child's head back and force the jaws open all by himself and at the same time look— unsuccessfully.

"Can I help?" asked a nurse, walking into the booth.

"Yes, hold his head back while I——"

But he reckoned without little Jakie who at that moment got one foot loose and let it fly, with the result that it not only dirtied the interne's nice white uniform, but caught him full on the chin.

"Cripes! You little devil, I'll——"

The nurse tried hard not to laugh, but only half succeeded.

"Transfer him to the nose and throat department," said the doctor and stalked out, a defeated man.

We moved along—there were some twenty in the group of third-year students—examining and discussing patients from the angle of diagnosis and treatment.

"You've got to try to put yourself in the other fellow's place," I told them, "and a good working rule is to treat them as you'd have them treat you. That's bromidic, of course, but try it. Remember, too, that children are different from adults. If adults can speak English or be made to understand you, they'll co-operate, but with children you need something more. You've got to get down to their level, and one way is to kid them. Children love to be joshed and laughed at and with and petted. Above all, try not to frighten them. Be gentle, and sometimes while you're talking to the mother, just reach out and casually and without looking give the kid a little hug or a pat on the head. You'll be surprised how he'll cuddle up to you."

"May I ask a question?" said one of the girls. "Do you tell people how sick they are?"

"Well, that's off the point at the moment, but people differ and so do conditions. I dare say you had cancer in mind?"

"Yes."

"Well——" but just then a house officer suggested that the group might be interested in a bad accident case that had just come in, and we adjourned to the emergency-room. We don't do that as a rule in dispensary work, even though the accident department is adjacent, because students are supposed to see the run of the mill cases, take their histories, and make examinations, and accident cases take too much of their time. Nevertheless, there are occasional ones of extreme interest, and the one in question illustrated surgical shock in high degree.

"He looks awfully pale, doesn't he?" said one of the boys.

"Hardly breathing," said another.

Nurses were scurrying about getting out bottles and apparatus for plasma. A doctor was carefully undoing the red, soppy emergency bandages that covered both of the man's lower legs.

"Got caught in some kind of machinery," he said, and then added: "Slipped." He did not take the bandages off, just undid them and looked.

"This man is in what we call a state of shock." I was

talking low." "And that's why we brought you to see him. His blood pressure is low, his pulse is weak, he looks like death, and death would come if they dealt with his injured legs without first giving him the plasma and perhaps blood that you see them getting ready for. I'm sorry we can't stay, but we'll try to come back in an hour or two, and maybe you'll see a different picture."

As luck had it a good opportunity presented itself to answer the question about telling people the whole truth and nothing but the truth. A woman of forty-seven had a lump in her left breast and though she looked and acted in an unconcerned way it was apparent that no word of what was being said escaped her. The student who took the history was reciting its highlights. "Patient is a housewife; always worked hard; never been especially ill; husband and two children living and well. Some three months ago accidentally noticed a small, hard lump in her left breast. No pain then, but some now. Lump's grown a bit. Patient says she's lost ten pounds, but does not feel ill."

"Did you make an examination?"

"Yes."

"Well?"

"Patient is a healthy-looking woman and examination really is negative until one comes to the breast where there is a hard lump about the size of a walnut. It isn't sensitive to the touch, it's pretty well outlined, and I think it's a cancer."

There was a dull silence and whereas the patient had been looking at the speaker, she was now looking at the floor—and had turned pale.

"I didn't ask you for your diagnosis, Miss Ellers, merely for your findings."

"But I thought——"

"You are beginners, of course, and perhaps I should have warned you about speaking too freely before patients in terms that they understand. I think it was you who posed the question about telling people all the truth, wasn't it?"

"Yes, and——"

"And now you have a partial answer, at least. This patient was somehow afraid she had a cancer, but was hoping against hope. Isn't that so, Mrs. Jones?"

"My doctor sent me here to make sure," she said in a very low voice.

"She's very much upset, as you can see, and if you had to give your diagnosis it would have been much better if you'd used the technical term of carcinoma.*

No one said anything.

"Plenty of people know what that is, but plenty don't, and in any case they aren't sure and therefore aren't quite as shocked as they would be at hearing the outright word."

"But isn't it best to tell them right out?" asked a boy.

"Yes and no. Some people can take it straight and others can't, and even when they ask for it and insist that they can, they may be bluffing or dead wrong. I've seen the thin, puny-looking one stand up and look it straight in the eye without faltering and I've seen the big, stalwart, blustering person collapse utterly. It's a moot point, this business of conveying all the truth to sick people and you've got to develop your own technique."

"I still don't understand," said a bewildered-looking fellow.

"No, you don't, and it will probably be some years before you do. All I can say is, put yourself in the other person's position and remember that there are other ways of telling

* It was a cancer and not an early one. Axillary glands were enlarged and hard.

them than by sheer bludgeoning. Sooner or later they've got to know the truth; that's certain. But sometimes they feel better if you give them a little time and let them figure it out for themselves. Doctoring is an art and after you've been about a bit you learn how to make patients ask you questions and in this manner give you an opportunity to make your point."

"But don't you ever come right out with it?" they persisted.

I couldn't help smiling. They were so naïve and fresh— and had such a long way to go.

"Sure, we tell them. Plenty of times. Flat out and even brutally. But if you'll watch you'll see that it's mostly when the case is bad or very urgent and the patient can't see or won't see or utterly refuses to face up to it—or, as happens in some cases, their relatives won't. We go to the mat with them then, regardless of consequences." That seemed to satisfy them. "We'll have more to say about this later on and we'll also have more to say about malignant growths in general, but it occurs to me to make one point right now because it is so important. You will recall that this lady knew she had a lump in her breast three months ago, but wasn't particularly worried about it, and didn't come to the hospital till just today. What would you think was the reason, Miss Ellers?"

"Why—uh——"

"What would you think, Mr. Joslyn?"

"Well, it wasn't big and—and——"

"And it did not hurt," I added. "That's one of the troubles with early malignancy; it doesn't hurt or it causes such little discomfort that the patient ignores it. In general, pain and fear make patients come running to doctors and hospitals, and it's a tragedy of the first water

that early cancer so often causes neither. Only as it pro-
gresses does it compel attention, and by that time it is often
too late. In breast growths, curiously enough, the ones that
hurt early are more often than not benign."

The group stood silent and I thought it wise to let the
lesson sink in for a moment.

"Now let's pass on to the next booth. What's the matter
with you, son?" I asked of a youngster lying on the table.

"Pain in my side."

"He's fifteen years old, doctor," said the student, "and
took sick yesterday with slight nausea, discomfort in the
pit of his stomach, radiating down to the right lower side,
and considerable pain there."

"Any other similar attacks?"

"One about four months ago."

"Temperature? Pulse?"

"101° by mouth; pulse 96. He didn't sleep last night and
hasn't eaten a thing."

"Did you examine him?"

"Yes, but there wasn't much but the tenderness."

"Nothing else?"

"His abdominal muscles are tight, if that's what you
mean."

"Nothing else?"

"Not that I noticed."

"Well, in a general sort of way a surgeon depends chiefly
on his eyes and his hands. Does that give you a lead?"

"I—uh—that is——"

"How does the boy look?" I asked, not wishing to delay
further.

"Oh, yes, of course. He looks rather ill."

"That he does, and practical doctors go a good deal by
looks and general demeanour and things like that—despite

all our wonderful tests and science. What would you think is wrong with this patient?'

"Appendicitis?

"In all probability. He could have other things, but appendicitis is chiefly an affection of youngsters, it is characterised by recurrent attacks, isn't so bad at first but develops progressively. What do you think we ought to do about him?"

"Operate, I suppose."

"Yes, it's best to take out inflamed appendices at the earliest possible moment—other things being equal—but, of course, we'll make sure of our diagnosis first by looking at the boy's blood and urine."

"And now, young lady, why are you here?" I was addressing a sallow-faced, scrawny young girl of about twenty-three, but it was her fat, plethoric-looking mother who replied.

"Our doctor says Mamie's got a goitre and needs an operation."

Mamie was busy twisting a soiled, damp handkerchief and had nothing to say. She wore plain metal-rimmed glasses that certainly did not add to her looks and she was the picture of unhappiness. Flat-chested, long thin neck, no obvious thyroid enlargement, straight black hair that was badly brushed—if at all—she looked so frightened and forlorn that I couldn't help wondering . . .

The student was saying that Mamie's mother and father were living and well, and so was a younger sister who had married two years before and had a baby. Mamie herself had always been rather delicate, didn't finish high school, went to work as a sales-girl in a department-store and quit when the war broke out to work in a factory. That made her tired, though, and after a few months she gave it up. Has not been doing anything but resting since, but still doesn't feel well, and all the doctor found was a small round lump, about as big as the end of one's thumb, in her thyroid gland.

"Did you find anything else?" I asked.

"No, sir."

"Did Dr. Guthrie go over this case with you?"

"Yes, sir, and he, too, says all she's got is the nodule."

"What's her pulse?"

"About normal, and so's her temperature. She isn't especially nervous, either—that is, like toxic goitre cases are supposed to be. That's what Dr. Guthrie said."

"Oh, but she is nervous," the plump mother said. "She cries and carries on and—and she won't eat sometimes. Mamie don't sleep none too good, neither; do you, dear?"

"No." That was the first word the girl had uttered.

"Tell me, Mamie," I said, turning to the patient, "don't you feel like working or——" but before I could finish, plump little Mother was oaring in again, or starting to, until there was nothing else to do but set her down.

"Madam," I said, "we'll get lots further if you'll compose yourself and let the girl talk for herself."

"But——"

"Please!" And she shut up—reluctantly.

"Now, Mamie, tell us what's bothering you chiefly. Don't you feel well? Are you worried? Have you no appetite?"

Tears stood in the girl's eyes but she didn't reply.

"Do you like the movies, Mamie, and do you sometimes go out with your boy friends?"

"Oh, Mamie's a home-body," interposed the irrepressible mother, coming forward to place a protecting arm about her daughter, "and me and Mr. Cruzy are her buddies."

That finished it and I took the group out to see another case—ostensibly.

"Now, Mr. Sellers, what do you make of Mamie?"

"Well, I don't rightly know except that she has got that little lump in her thyroid. Her heart and lungs are O.K. and she seems to be generally all right."

"Anybody else got ideas?"

"She certainly doesn't look happy," said one of the girls.

"That undoubtedly is true. What would you do about her?"

"I guess I'd take the lump out and see what happens."

"You could do that, of course, but suppose you go over there and call that mother of hers out and engage her in conversation while I slip in and get the real low-down from the girl. Then we'll be able to act intelligently."

It was the old, old story. Unattractive older girl jealous of attractive younger sister. Dominating, misunderstanding mother. The poor thing burst into tears the moment the mother was out of earshot and needed little urging to spill the whole pathetic story.

"You've got to know something about life," I remarked to the students immediately following the interview, "if you're going to be a doctor, and that's one of the reasons why I think dispensary work is so important. You see life in the raw here and all kinds of people with all sorts of problems. Moreover, they come in fresh, right from the street, and it is here that you watch experienced doctors get their stories—starting from scratch—make examinations and come to conclusions without any of the frills or scientific tests that are usually made in the wards and private rooms of hospitals where there are assistants and technicians and facilities. We do make some of these tests, but it is usually after we have demonstrated the cases to you and pretty much made up our minds.

"And this young girl is a case in point. You didn't get the true story, Mr. Sellers, but that is excusable in you. It is not so excusable in the doctor who sent her in for operation. She has the lump and some day it had best be removed—but not now. It's quiescent and has nothing to do with her trouble. The girl is utterly unhappy, and that's true of lots of people who frequent doctors' offices and hospitals—nothing else. They come a cropper, too, in many instances, because doctors are busy and sometimes miss the real point. That is why, among other things, we see so many operations that fail to bring results."

"Wouldn't you think it wise to send Mamie to the psychiatrists?" asked young Sellers.

"I would if I didn't have a little confidence in myself."

The students were smiling.

"I told that girl to get out of her home and be on her own. If possible she should leave this town and go to work elsewhere."

"Why so?" inquired Miss Long.

"So she won't see that sister, her husband and baby and, in addition—perhaps above all—be free of her mouthy mother."

"Do you think she will?"

"That's hard to say, but I took another step and it occurs to me to ask if any of you would have an idea what that is?"

"You eased off her mother, or will," said one boy, and I couldn't help laughing.

"I'd love nothing better, son, but she's so pleased with herself and so certain she's done a swell job by her daughter that I wouldn't get to first base with her. No, that's not it."

They seemed nonplussed.

"Remember what I said about doctors being practical? Does that help you?"

They had no answer.

"I told Miss Mamie to sneak out one morning later in the week and come up here by herself. If she were a girl of seventeen or eighteen I wouldn't dare do that, but she's twenty-three and quite of age. The girl smiled for the first time at that, and without doubt she'll be here. I expect to talk to her again myself, but, more than that, there is a very understanding woman in the social service department, and I expect to turn the girl over to her. Mamie might do very well, and she wouldn't be the first of her kind we've saved."

"It's been a rather long and exhausting morning for some of you, but doctors have to get used to that, and so, before you leave, let's go and see that man we left in the accident room an hour or so ago."

"Haven't they taken him to the operating-room by this time?" asked one of the boys.

"He looked pretty much done in to me," I replied, "and generally speaking the time and place to deal with shock is right where patients come in. They don't tolerate moving about very well, and every once in a while you see one of them die just from too much handling."

The man was lying on the same table and in the same position as when we first saw him, but by now he presented a very different picture.

"He certainly looks better, doesn't he?" said one of the girls.

"How so?" I asked.

"His colour's better, for one thing, and he's awake. You

can see him breathing and—and the look of death has all but gone."

"That's fine. What else?"

"Well, I noticed him smile just now at something the nurse whispered to him, and he also answered her."

"Very good, and if you'll take a look at this chart the doctor has just handed me, you'll see how nicely his blood pressure has risen and how his pulse first steadied and then began to fall. It's really wonderful, and I have no doubt that as soon as all that plasma has passed into his veins and he picks up a bit more, they'll put him to sleep and fix up his legs."

"Won't they have to move him to the operating-room for that?"

"Not necessarily. Accident rooms of modern hospitals are equipped to do most anything these days, and house officers are specially trained. People don't know that generally because so little is said of it in the lay press, but it would be well if they did know."

It had been a good morning, and I trusted that my students had picked up some valuable points as we went along.

8

ACCIDENT ROOM

THE POLICEMAN STOOD LOOKING AT THE BEDRAGGLED APPEAR-
ance of the man lying on the table in the hospital's accident
room.

"We picked him up unconscious on the street, doc, and
the way he smells of likker, I guess he's plain drunk."

"Yes, sure," said the interne, as he felt the patient's pulse,
then lifted the eyelids to take a look at the pupils, and,
finally, opened collar and shirt preparatory to listening to
the heart.

"Shall we take him along, doc?" inquired the policeman.

The interne didn't answer.

"Might as well let him sleep it off at the station house,"
persisted the officer.

The doctor absent-mindedly removed the stethoscope
from his ears and stood back from the table as if to get a
better look at the man. A nurse had hurried in and,
noticing that the lights above the table had not been turned
on full, snapped the extra switch, then began to get things
out of the glassed-in chests that lined the walls—towels,
gauze, hot-water-bottles, hypodermics and other syringes,
stomach tube, blood-transfusion kit—the usual things that
might be needed in an emergency.

"What say, doc?"

"I say we'd better have a little more of a look. Nurse,
would you please get ready to wash out his stomach?"

"Yes, doctor. I'm getting things out now. Plain water?"

"Yes."

"Hot or cold?"

"Lukewarm, I suppose."

"Aw, now, doc——"

"Listen, officer," interrupted the interne, "I agree that the old fellow is liquored up, or was, but he looks awfully pale and his breathing is shallow. Pulse is slow, too. We'd better see. Suppose you and your buddie there, come back in about an hour, or call in."

"O.K.," said the policeman, with obvious disgust. "You're the boss, but—come on, Joe," and he and Joe left.

One hour later the old man was still on the table. Two hours later he was off it, but still in the same room, under observation. They had placed him on a bed in one corner, and the way he was quietly sleeping it looked as if it had been only a jag. They'd washed out lots of smelly stuff from his stomach and given him a stimulant—a small dose —and he had reacted somewhat. Nurses had removed shoes and filthy, sodden clothes, and as he lay there in fresh hospital dress, face washed clean, he was almost presentable.

"His colour's better, doctor, and so is his pulse," said the nurse as she jotted down the notes on her chart.

"Breathing better, too, isn't he?" the young doctor remarked.

"Yes, sir. Deeper. He moves occasionally and groans a little."

"Has Dr. Sparks been in yet?"

"He was here half an hour ago when you were on the ward, and said he thought you were wise to hold the man."

Dr. Grant's face lighted up. "Say anything else?"

"No, sir."

"Nothing about a possible skull fracture?"

"I didn't hear him."

"Well——" and the young doctor left, saying he would return shortly.

Young Dr. Grant was carrying out express orders "to make sure and not be stampeded by anyone". It had always been one of my ambitions to handle an accident service, and when Wingate Hospital came under my direction—surgical and otherwise—I was determined that no chances were to be taken. Alcoholic breath does not necessarily spell drunkenness, and more than once newspapers have featured the story of a man dying unattended in his cell only a few hours after having been superficially examined by hospital attachés.

"To receive emergency cases off the streets, the results of accident or sudden catastrophic illness, involves a heavy duty," I had said to the boys, "and hospitals are well advised to play as safe as possible. No better training-ground can be found for young doctors than the accident rooms because there you see life in all its phases, that is where minutes, even split seconds, may count and where, finally, judgment, self-confidence, knowledge, and common sense all rolled into one make for success or failure. You'll have to learn how to size up the case that can be fixed up promptly and dismissed and you'll have to learn how to pick out the one that can't. It isn't easy. That's the reason you who are beginners are instructed to call your immediate superior when you are in doubt. If the two of you can't decide, a staff man is to be summoned and the matter left in his hands. Under no circumstances are you to dismiss a doubtful case."

"What if it's a small cut, a busted head, or simple fracture?" asked one young man. "Are we to handle them on our own?"

"How many fractures have you set, doctor?" I asked.

"None, but——"

"How many wounds have you repaired?"

"I've helped in a few."

"Well, would you want your own broken arm or bashed-in face, or that of your mother or your sister, handled by one of such limited experience as yours?"

"Naturally not, but——"

"But what, son?"

"Well, I——" he began.

"You don't mind my calling you 'son', do you? After all, you are hardly more than a boy."

He grinned and collapsed. His mates laughed. None of them spoke and I continued. "What Dr. Gorman had in mind was the need for a fellow's doing things himself and without supervision. Isn't that it, Gorman?"

"Yes, sir."

"Well, that will come later. First we will give you a definite course of training and then we will let you do things under someone's watchful eye. Gradually, only gradually, will you be on your own, and even then only to the degree that is warranted by your ability and experience."

Each new batch of internes got the same lecture, and there was always one, sometimes two, who was rarin' to go regardless. To safeguard the patient, the hospital, and the man himself, these men were put on accident service later, and though they didn't know it, their work and actions were especially screened.

The youngster Gorman had average ability and proved to be an excellent worker; but he lacked sympathy and his judgment was atrocious—so bad, in fact, that he finally got us into trouble with the city welfare department. Twice during a terribly stormy November night he sent a distraught woman home with her baby, saying it wasn't sick enough to be admitted. At 11 o'clock its temperature was 103°, at 3.30 it was 104½°, and I don't know what it was at 5.30 when the neighbours took a hand and raised a row. When it finally was admitted at 6.30 in the morning its temperature was 105°—rectally, it is true—and it had an ear that badly needed puncturing.

"Tell me, Gorman," I said some hours later, "just how high does a patient's temperature have to go before you think he's ill?"

"I—uh—guess I made a mistake."

"And just what conditions in general must prevail before you feel it necessary or wise to admit a patient?"

The boy was on the spot and there was no point in bearing down, except that I was so exasperated.

"I don't mind your missing the ear condition because we all make mistakes, but to miss the human values is inexcusable. Doctors, of all people, should take them into account. It was bad enough for you to send that woman out with her baby the first time, but to do it again four hours later and on such a night is beyond my comprehension."

"All beds were full."

"What's that got to do with it? They could have put up one or she could have remained in the accident room. If you had only called the resident and put it up to him!"

Two days later, when the Board of Welfare sent the inevitable letter of inquiry, I stated the facts, admitted that we had done an unconscionable thing and offered no excuses. That must have surprised them, because they wrote back that the attitude was something new in hospital administration and that they were pleased. They felt sure appropriate measures would be taken to prevent a repetition and therefore the matter would be dropped.

We did take measures to tighten up, but it is impossible to eliminate the human equation, though you can minimise it. Dr. Gorman was not dropped. He could hardly have got another interneship if he had been, and the result would have been to foist a resentful, untutored man on the public to do further harm. Instead, he was kept on, and with relentless pressure made to see the error of his ways.

"You learn more by mistakes than by successes in this game, Gorman, or at least you can if you're smart." We were having a talk over cigarettes and coffee. "The only trouble is that it's the other man's life and well-being that are at stake, and you have to keep putting yourself in the other fellow's position. Understand?"

"Yes, sir, and I am grateful for the pains being taken with me."

He came to be the safest man we had and made a great success in practice later on.

Early one Sunday morning, when things were unusually quiet, I touched the bell at the accident entrance, walked in, stretched myself out on the table, and awaited results. Three minutes later a nurse hurried in and two minutes after that a doctor appeared.

"Just checking up on the system," I remarked, in answer to their surprised looks. "Now let's investigate your equipment. How many clamps have you got, large and small? Pull them all out, and while you're at it get out whatever else you have."

Dutifully, the nurse complied, and after that she asked if

I'd like to see the supply of sterile gauze, towels, and things.
"Sure thing," I said. "And as long as we are at it, how
about your drugs? Got your hypos loaded, sterile, and
ready for use? Got plenty of salt solution and glucose?
And how about insulin? Any of that on hand? Got
plasma, sulfas, and penicillin?"

Doctor and nurse went to work and in short order had
everything out, even to the tracheotomy tube that isn't
used so often nowadays, but sometimes saves the day.
Splints and plaster and bandages and tourniquets; they
had everything in good measure, but were chagrined when
I inquired about an extra high-powered battery lamp that
every accident room ought to have in case something un-
foreseen should happen to the main electric current.

"I never heard of such a thing," said the interne. "We
have a couple of flash-lamps," handing one to me.

"They have one in each operating-room, doctor," the
nurse said. "Large, specially made things that have their
own batteries and give out good light."

"That's what I ordered."

"They never had one down here."

"But can't the lights go out here, too, and couldn't it
happen while you're handling a desperate accident case?"

"Of course. I'll have one ordered immediately, sir."

"Please do, and meantime better bring one down from
the operating-room till it comes. And test it out before you
put it away."

"Yes, sir."

"I haven't seen the orderly. Got one, haven't you?"

"Yes, sir, but he's off on Sundays and we have to get one
from the first hall in case of need."

That evening, at seven o'clock, the accident bell rang
again, and this time it wasn't a test. A private aeroplane

had crashed and the pilot and three passengers, all badly injured, practically swamped the place. Internes sent for residents and residents put in calls for staff men, nurses swarmed around and almost the whole hospital personnel mobilised to the work of bringing the shocked and unconscious back to a semblance of life. Hot-water-bottles and blankets were used to warm them, bottles of salt solution and glucose, all prepared and ready, were brought out for intravenous use—also plasma—and in short order the machinery was clicking.

You can't do operations and set fractures—or even give anæsthetics—while your patient is in shock because if you do he'll keep fading out and die. Many people don't know that and cause a lot of trouble by insisting that something be done, getting in the way while efforts at resuscitation are going on. This happened the night of that aeroplane accident; relatives and friends were milling around, crying and talking and beseeching doctors and nurses to do their best when they already were, and the place was in an uproar by the time I got there. It wouldn't have happened if it hadn't been on a Sunday evening when half the resident staff was off duty. It shouldn't have happened then, because the police officers on duty should have shooed out everyone except those actually working. They did eventually, at my behest, and for several hours all I did was to act as ringmaster in a four-ring circus.

It was a mess and convinced me that hospitals generally pay too little attention to emergency work, erroneously leaving its detailed management to junior staff men or residents of limited experience. In this case, time was lost getting the older men and putting them to work; but, more than that, in this comparatively small outlying hospital everybody was crowded in on top of everybody else—until the two worst cases could be moved up to the general operating-rooms. If we'd had the extra rooms that we got later on—with beds in them and general equipment for treatment and observation—things would have been much simplified. All four patients lived, but one had an awfully tight squeeze.

We could improve our own procedure, but we could do nothing to mitigate the iniquities of custom and superstition among the patients. When I was a third-year student I saw for the first time a typical case in point. A mother with a dirty-looking little bundle in her arms came shrieking into the accident rooms, closely followed by three other dishevelled creatures, all equally excited. When the young house officer started to take the bundle out of the woman's arms she drew back and let out a yelp that could have been heard a block away.

"But, lady——" the doctor started to say.

"No, no! Don't touch! Don't touch!" the woman cried.

"But——"

"I show, I show," and with that she uncovered what looked to me like a negro baby, only that didn't make sense because the mother was white.

"For God's sake!" the interne cried, after one look. "Not again! This is the third time in two weeks."

"What's the third time?" I asked, taking a closer look.

"Ink. They throw ink on them when their kids get burned. It's an old Spanish custom or something," he said, as he guided the frantic mother towards a table and began to help her peel the baby out of its coverings.

I couldn't believe my eyes, but there it was, black ink splashed all over the child's face, neck, arms, and clothes until you couldn't see what was burned and what wasn't.

"You'd think they'd have better sense," said an exasper-

D

ated nurse as she elbowed the mother out of the way and started mopping the child's face with warm water. "But no, someone's told them that ink is the best thing for burns. Look, doctor, this child's only been mildly scalded, at least in the face——"

"It's chest a bit worse, I guess—the shirt sticks—but it's hard to tell because of the ink."

And so they washed and they scrubbed as gently as possible, but the child suffered, none the less, and the mother wailed and jabbered, never once realising that she had made a bad situation worse by her unusual remedy. I saw similar exhibitions as the years passed, but thanks to education the practice has all but disappeared.

Among the most interesting of all cases were the "repeats", such as the stout, middle-aged woman that the police were likely to bring in almost any Saturday night, her lips so swollen that she could hardly speak, eyes blacked, nose bleeding, a sight to turn the stomach. The chief nurse knew her well and always greeted her cheerfully, although with disgust.

"Well, Mary," she said, as she helped undo the woman's dress, "it's you, as I live—though this time I almost didn't recognise you."

Mary grunted, half cocked one eye and tried to smile.

"When are you going to divorce that no-good man of yours?"

Mary just shook her head.

"He's a good man, that's what she'd say if she could talk. Eh, Mary? And doesn't mean any harm. Just a bit too much liquor and his having to take it out on someone. That it, Mary?" The nurse began to bathe the poor thing's battered features.

"And Monday morning, bright and early, she'll be in

court with the money she's scrimped to pay her drunken husband's fine. Us women!" She made a wry face as she turned the case over to an assistant nurse.

I always liked the accident rooms, even as a student, and haunted them as much as the internes would permit, but others felt differently about them.

"You don't have to do this kind of work to be a good doctor," a class-mate of mine said one day, "and I'm going to skin out of every bit I can."

We had just seen a little girl of seven who had been badly crushed by a truck. By the time they found the mother and brought her to the hospital, the child was dead. It wasn't a pretty sight, and no man would voluntarily witness the scene that followed.

"I don't know about its making a good doctor of you," I said, "but such things do happen, and somebody's got to do what's possible. Now you take that poor woman. She's going to be a wreck for days, maybe weeks, and the doctor who attends her will be better able to help her if he's seen things and done them. Anyway, that's how it looks to me."

The accident rooms are, I believe, the best places in the world for finding out what people think. For instance, there was the factory fire that taught me a great deal about the police. It happened years later and was occasioned by an explosion of chemicals that blew out the brick walls and injured civilians as well as firemen. We needed blood badly, so badly that the call for volunteers went out. Within the hour volunteers began to appear, among them a number of policemen. In fact, the police were the best of the lot, and we took the blood of several. When the company offered to pay them, they were deeply hurt.

"What do they think we are, scavengers?" one of them said to me.

"Certainly not," I replied, "but after all, you don't owe these injured people anything."

"I know, but people get the idea cops are hard guys and——"

We let it go at that.

9

EXPERIMENTAL SURGERY

COMING FROM THE FOUR CORNERS OF THE LAND—ALSO FROM
foreign lands—and converging on Baltimore and the Johns
Hopkins Hospital is a veritable parade of children who
never before had hope. Now there is hope for them, and
it has come through brilliant experimental work done on
dogs within the last few years. The children are called
"blue babies" in the vernacular, but that just means that
they weren't able to breathe properly when they were born
and so their skin and lips were blue, and remained so.
What they had was a congenital heart malformation that
prevented blood from circulating through the lungs in
sufficient quantity to give the normal amount of oxygen.

Dr. Alfred Blalock, Professor of Surgery, and Dr.
Helen B. Taussig, Associate Professor of Pediatrics at the
Hopkins, did most of the work jointly,[*] and, like other
surgeons who do experimental work, they chose dogs because they were most suitable from the standpoint of avail-
ability, size and anatomy comparable to that of the human
being. It would be out of character in a work like this to
give details of the operative procedure developed, but it
concerned an increased pulmonary blood flow that resulted

---

[*] (1) Blalock, A., and Taussig, H. B.: "The Surgical Treatment of Malformation of the Heart in Which There Is Pulmonary Stenosis or Pulmonary
Atresia." *J.A.M.A.*, 128:188, May 19, 1945.

(2) Blalock, Alfred: "Effects of an Artificial Ductus Arteriosus on Experimental Cyanosis and Anoxemia." *Archives of Surgery*, Vol. 52, No. 3,
pp. 247–252, March, 1946.

in satisfactory oxygenation, and it worked beyond expectations. The blue were blue no longer. The fact that the entire operation has to be done within the chest and that in the nature of things the little patients are not the best surgical risks only heightens the surgeon's interest—and perhaps raises his own blood pressure. I leave to your imagination the colossal amount of work all this entailed.

But when you consider that hitherto these children had little to look forward to but a life of semi-invalidism or worse, that they couldn't run and jump and play like other children, because if they did they collapsed from shortness of breath, that few of them lived to become adults, I say when you consider this outcome as against the full, normal life this new operation bids fair to give them, you will surely agree that the sacrifice of a comparatively few animals was more than justified. The only pity of it is that not all forms of congenital heart malformation are amenable to the operation and that the patients have to be selected with extreme care lest changes that have already taken place render their chances of survival too slim to make the operation worth while.

I leave out of consideration the fact that the operation is too formidable for the average surgeon to undertake, because, in time, specialists in every major clinic will be trained to do it just as they've been trained to do other unusual things. And surely the field thus opened up will be widened to include conditions not now amenable to operative interference. I might, however, remark that the Balock-Taussig procedure is but another indication that surgeons can be builders if they put their minds to it and give up some of their defeatist tendencies.

It is instinctive for man to try to better himself, and no single group has made greater effort in that direction than the doctors—or been more harassed, misunderstood, even persecuted for their pains. Yet the work went on, and now we see everywhere throughout the land great laboratories devoted to investigation work of different kinds. The one we have at the Hopkins for experimental surgery is called the Hunterian Laboratory—named in honour of John Hunter, famous in medicine in a former era. It was started by Harvey Cushing, renowned investigator himself and brain surgeon at Hopkins in the early years of this century.

Cushing always insisted that surgery in general, but animal experimentation in particular, entailed a heavy responsibility, and that if doctors were to be permitted to engage in it they owed especial duty to the animal—his welfare, his food, his care, particularly his living quarters. He placed work in the Hunterian Laboratory on the highest possible scientific and moral level and no greater service was ever done the medical profession, because so many laboratories of a similar nature, then and now, followed his lead in the maintenance of high standards of management. He saw clearly that scientific progress along certain lines would be slowed up greatly without animal experimentation, but he also saw the danger attendant on such methods, particularly the antagonism of an unenlightened society.

To make friends for his laboratory, to woo possible objectors, and also for the sake of animals in general, he established at the Hunterian a sort of consultation and treatment service for privately owned pets, and by the time I began to work in the Laboratory there was no question of the good will being built up. It was all new and exhilarating to me because I had never been inside such a place before, much less treated private patients of the animal kingdom. The nearest I'd come to it was the medical and surgical aid they had had me give pigs, dogs, cows, horses, and mules out on my father's farm.

Cushing was fond of animals, dogs in particular. He'd often drop what he was doing to look at a mongrel's sore foot or a bulldog's torn neck or a prize dog's ear that for unknown reasons wouldn't stand up as it should. He'd operate on them personally if they needed it and he had time; if he hadn't, he'd have his laboratory interne do it or give it to me or one of the other doctors.

The love and devotion those people had for their pets— and their gratitude—was plain to read in their faces. One day we'd all been out to lunch and I was the first of the doctors back. Sitting in the corridor was a poor, bedraggled boy of eight, holding the worst-looking, dirtiest shaggy-haired pup in his arms, the tears streaming down his cheeks.

"What's the matter, sonny?" I inquired.

"His dog got run over, doctor," said Charlie, my laboratory helper. "It looks bad."

"Well, bring him in here and let's have a look at him."

The boy wailed louder and wouldn't move.

"He somehow knows of Dr. Cushing," Charlie added, grinning, "and says nobody's going to touch his dog but him."

And nobody did, either—even if the Master couldn't perform a miracle. The poor kid carried his deceased friend home an hour or so later, and I don't think any of us did very good work that afternoon. Dr. Cushing offered the little fellow another dog, but he just shook his head sadly and left.

It wasn't only the neighbours' pets who came in as private patients. News of the service spread far and wide and many sick animals were brought or sent in from a distance. One lady from Virginia sent her pet pug in with a personal attendant, who deposited his charge with us and promptly went on a binge. The dog had a specially constructed box all lined with pale blue satin with padding to prevent injury during transit! It was the fattest, most supercilious, good-for-nothing pug you ever saw, and all she had wrong was a small benign tumour in a very special place! We took it off promptly, but it was days before her caretaker showed up in fit condition to escort the dog home.

No charge was made for any service, but if one wished to make a contribution to the Laboratory it was gratefully accepted. I once saw a little girl give twenty cents and a man give a dollar. There were many more substantial gifts. Of course we heard rumblings from time to time from licensed veterinary doctors who objected to the competition, but they never became vocal. Occasionally one of them paid us a visit, and in general a friendly spirit was maintained. In more than one instance dogs that were aged or in pain were brought in by their devoted owners with the injunction that we sacrifice them painlessly—which we did.

The Laboratory could not, under the city ordinance, get animals from the pound, and so had to rely on the good offices of boys and men who chanced upon stray dogs and brought them in. At first they received fifty cents for small dogs and seventy-five cents for big ones, but the price was gradually increased to two dollars each. And at that there were times, due to the activities of the Society for the Prevention of Cruelty to Animals, when we had none. The ladies and gentlemen of that organisation refused to be comforted despite invitation to inspect the work going on in the Laboratory and despite explanation of its urgency and importance. Dr. Cushing's own work on the brain made no appeal to them, nor did Dr. Halsted's work on aneurisms. The human values involved did not seem to be important. From time to time they would picket all four street corners around the Laboratory, and everyone who came along with a dog was arrested. More than once the work of the Labortory was entirely stopped. They went before the state legislature, too, not once but repeatedly, and it took all the persuasive eloquence of Dr. Welch and Dr. Cushing to prevent crippling legislation. Occasionally the whole medical profession of the community had to be mobilised. Recent years have seen a change for the better, but even now there are rumblings here and in other states. Only a year or so ago there was need for intensive action before the legislature.

Not all the dogs we got were "stray"—or perhaps one might put it, "stray of their own accord". You could usually tell when a dog had been a member of a good home, and when that kind turned up the keeper refused to take him. The need was great, however, and with the supply nearly always at low level and with the boys crossing their hearts that they found the pup, he couldn't always scrutinise too carefully. He did, however, try to obey the Laboratory rule, which was that no dog should be used until two full days had elapsed from the hour of reception. This was to give time for people to come and look for pets—a privilege freely accorded and many times accepted. It also was for the purpose of observing the animal, for it was a waste of time and effort, material and money to work on an unfit animal, especially one that was ill.

This procedure worked out very well in general, but the head keeper wasn't always there, and occasionally there was a mistake. Such a one happened to me. The animal was a big St. Bernard that Charlie, my laboratory helper, chose because my work at the moment was on blood vessels, and the bigger the dog the bigger his vessels and the easier to work with. The operation was hardly over and the animal put downstairs in its cage when suddenly there appeared the big, strapping baker who supplied the Laboratory with a special kind of corn bread the dogs liked. His dog had disappeared, his lovely Brunhilda, and he was in a rage.

"Any of you guys seen a big, brown, long-haired St. Bernard?" he cried, barging into the Laboratory. "Here, Brunhilda! Here, Brunhilda! I bet one of them low-down skunks 'at brings dogs in here stole her!"

I was washing up at the sink and Charlie was cleaning the instruments. We both recognised the description at the same time. Poor Charlie was worried—the baker could have broken him in two with his bare hands.

"Quick, Charlie," I whispered. "Get down there and put a towel or something in front of that dog's cage and then beat it." And for once Charlie did as told without argument, while I hurriedly wiped my hands and rushed after him. I knew the baker would go downstairs hollering his lungs out for his Brunhilda, but I also knew she couldn't answer him because she was still under ether! If he didn't see her—and it was late and there were lots of cages—I guessed that he would wait until the next day and then Jimmie, head keeper and arch soother-of-owners-of-stray-dogs-that-hadn't-exactly-strayed, perhaps could straighten things out. Provided the estimable Brunhilda didn't get pneumonia or die from my operation.

I don't believe I ever was so eager for a dog to recover, and I know Charlie went to church and prayed. He didn't show up until it was reported to him by special messenger that the crisis had been weathered. Jimmie did his usual stuff, even to the point of keeping Dr. Cushing from hearing about it; the lovely Brunhilda was no worse for wear; and the reunion between her and the baker was touching. It cost me ten dollars, though—five for Jimmie and five for the baker.

Every such laboratory has its Jimmie or Steve or Albert —general indispensable factotum who rules with a rod of iron. Ours was a little, thin, wiry man with pale, watery eyes, a moth-eaten, droopy moustache and a voice that was tired and soft until the dogs began sounding off in fierce chorus. Then Jimmie would give out one loud "Shet up!" with a peculiar growling quality in it that his charges recognised and instinctively obeyed. It literally rang through the place and there would be sudden quiet. It might be broken, but only by individual yelps—never by the chorus. They knew better.

Yet Jimmie never beat them or used strong arm methods. The most he ever did was walk in among the pack in the gathering pens, grab a ringleader and maybe give him a cuff over the ear. It was a strange thing to watch. He was fearless, and big dog, little dog, mean or treacherous, he waded right in without hesitation when there was a fight or other trouble. That's why the dogs liked him and quieted down at his command. That, together with the fact that he fed them. I once saw him walk into a pen to kill a dog with rabies with nothing in his hand but a small hammer. One of the doctors suggested shooting, and another felt that the proper way would be to catch the poor thing with the usual broomhandle and noose, and chloroform him; but Jimmie took orders only from Dr. Cushing in matters of importance, and he wasn't there. Jimmie just opened the Dutch door and walked in, and when the dog, a fair-sized mongrel, leaped at him, he struck him in the head with the hammer and it was all over.

Experimental work of any kind is exacting, at times tedious, and it is just as important to observe and study one's errors and mistakes as one's successes. You start with an idea and work out your own method of procedure. Sometimes you hit it correctly at the start, but sometimes you don't and have to begin all over—maybe several times. Occasionally things work out perfectly and success appears to be just around the corner. Then you find you have overlooked some little thing or not thought of this or that, or maybe did something one way when it should have been done another way, and the whole experiment fails. It is tantalising and requires infinite patience, extreme attention to detail, ability to change pace and tactics, courage to admit mistakes, and, above all, honesty.

In more recent times the Hunterian Laboratory has been divided into small rooms where individuals can carry on their work undisturbed and in private. Perhaps that's best, but in the early days there was just the one big room where investigators worked at tables alongside each other—even including the Professor, Dr. Halsted. It was a high privilege to watch him work, and one couldn't miss his meticulous search for causes of his errors and failures.

I can't vouch for it, but there was a story about how the Professor forgot to keep an appointment for an important operation in Washington because he had to operate on a dog. With assistants who were to accompany him cooling their heels and hospital attachés running around frantically looking for him, there he was blithely at work in the

Hunterian, completely oblivious to all things else. When reminded finally of the great lady waiting for her operation, he remarked that he was sorry, but he didn't have time that day and couldn't really say when he would. Perhaps if the lady would come to Baltimore he'd get around to her, but it wasn't really important; there were so many other surgeons.

I spent five years working in the Hunterian Laboratory, and they were among the happiest years of my life. Later in my career when problems arose, I went back and tried my hand again—not once but several times, and always with pleasure and satisfaction. Not all the work turned out as intended. Once I worked on a problem for two solid years, only to give it up in the end—a complete failure. Once, too, I had an idea that looked good and was good and all went well, but a man named Jacobaeus over in Sweden (or was it Norway?) got the same idea at the same time and beat me to publication. It's surprising how often that happens—men in different clinics, different parts of the world, getting the same ideas and doing the same work at the same time. It seems uncanny, but the answer is probably simple enough—the gradual procession of scientific advance that projects new things into the focus of investigators intent on their work, however widely separated they may be.

The idea I speak of concerned diagnosis of intra-abdominal conditions. Merely by making a little nick through the skin and muscles and by shoving in a narrow, hollow tube, that was long enough to be moved around, you could see what the conditions were—as they do in the bladder examinations. A headlight or perhaps a tiny little electric light within the tube would furnish illumination. With this apparatus the examination could be carried out quickly under very light anæsthesia. If successful it might avoid many big exploratory operations. The trials worked beautifully; the dogs suffered no ill effects; Dr. Cushing liked it and suggested trial on a patient in the hospital— and there came the hitch. They were only mildly interested over there and refused trial. Not being launched in practice sufficiently to have patients of my own, and not yet having other hospital affiliations, I could do nothing but go on for the time being with other problems of greater importance. For it is customary to make a so-called clinical trial of your experiment before publishing the results.

And then it happened—some two or three months later. A man working four thousand miles away, of whom none of us had ever heard, came out with almost the identical experimental work I had done, only he had access to clinical material. He cited numbers of successful cases. Shortly afterwards, my clinical trial was permitted and when it worked and looked promising an article was written and published—too late for priority. No, the episode did not break my heart—it wasn't that important— but new and original ideas are not just pulled out of the air, and it is worth mentioning that that bit of work was the forerunner of today's well-recognised procedure with the impressive name of Peritoneoscopy. More recent investigators have devised a beautifully perfected apparatus to give better and more precise vision.

I speak only for myself in the business of experimental surgery, and although I regard myself as hardened to all phases of surgery, there were occasions when I couldn't go it any more and had to quit for a time. You have got to steel yourself to operate on dogs—more than on any other animal. Not so much because you are making them suffer, as because you feel you are doing them a low-down, dirty trick—and they are so forgiving. I don't think it would be half so bad if they didn't forgive you. It's different with humans. They can talk and bawl you out fight back, and they do plenty of both if things don't go to their liking. Moreover, they don't have to be operated on if they don't want to. That is, the adults don't. Little children do, and in a way are in the same position as the dogs—and they, too, have a way of forgiving you that can be disconcerting.

There was that sleek little black-haired cocker spaniel that found her way to my operating table. I hadn't noticed her until she was under anæsthetic and I was busy with the first part of a two-stage stomach operation. She was so friendly and pleasant-mannered afterwards that I knew she must have come from a good home, but Jimmie said "No", and when Jimmie spoke that was the end of the discussion. I was pleased at her beautiful recovery. She was, too, and we became great friends. I must admit, though, that it had not occurred to me to look at her pelvic organs at operation. Why should I? So I was quite unprepared for the family she presented me with some three or four weeks later. They were her pride and joy, those pups, and I never did do the second stage of the operation.

I don't know how wise it would be to refuse permission to do experimental surgery on dogs unless a surgeon owned a dog himself, but it's worth thinking about. We've never been without one or two in my family and they always have been our close friends, especially Hans. A big, black Doberman pinscher, strong as an ox, pleasant and polite around the house, he could do everything but talk and could almost do that when things didn't go his way.

Hans loved to fight. Most Doberman pinschers do. It's in their blood. It was in Hans's, certainly, and the bigger the dog the quicker he'd go after him and the harder he'd fight. He was a good fighter too, and regularly patrolled the neighbourhood out in the country where we lived. I didn't like it, and several times told him he'd come a cropper. But he wouldn't listen.

So Hans went his stubborn way and, like all fighters, began to take in more territory. He'd be marked up from time to time, but it never was bad and he seemed well able to take care of himself. Then I began to notice evidence of his coming out second-best in some of his fights. To clinch matters, the children commenced calling me in consultation. Hans was getting older, but couldn't be brought to realise it.

A neighbour had started a kennel. He specialised in pedigree German police dogs, and bad though the outlook was for Hans, nothing happened because it was a real kennel, with well-built houses and runways, and all. From time to time the night air was rent with terrible barking and one could tell that serious trouble would arise if the wire barriers didn't hold, but they did. Then, our neighbour made an addition to his kennel. He bought one of the biggest Great Danes I'd ever seen—and not only that, he let him run.

The neighbour was very friendly and insisted that his dog, Etzelson, was nothing but a big, clumsy, overgrown pup, who wouldn't harm a flea. He denied emphatically trying to keep Hans off his place, but I had my doubts and forthwith instituted night restrictions—all to no purpose. Hans wouldn't have it, the children wouldn't have it, nobody would have it, and I was an outcast. That is, until Hans turned up early one morning with his neck ripped open. Then you should have heard the carrying on and the crying and the insistence that I do something and quick.

"He's bleedin' to death, Daddy. He's bleedin' bad. Can't you help him?" cried Pete, getting me out of bed.

Hans had very definitely come out second-best. Furthermore, the old fraud knew it was his own fault and I'd have sworn he deliberately winked at me as he lay there outside the kitchen door being petted and fussed over by the entire household. He didn't grudge me my innings, either. At last I became a hero. The children danced off and scrambled to do my every bidding. The hired man was fetching and carrying; the cook was solicitous; and Mrs. Bernheim, confessed that maybe they should have listened to me. I had to take Hans over to the Hunterian Laboratory for a considerable repair job and for three whole days I was No. 1 man in my own home—a long time for any father! I'm sorry to say Hans didn't learn his lesson. We tried to get the neighbour to pen up his dog or even get rid of him —other people had reason to complain, too—but he refused, and despite our efforts to control Hans he would go out and go over there.

Towards the end Hans developed a growth on his left hind leg and it took me one solid hour of the best operating I ever did at the Hunterian Laboratory to remove it—without crippling him. He knew it was hard for me to have to operate on him and not only went to sleep without a struggle, but licked my hand repeatedly by way of thanks the moment he woke up. He lived two years after that, but fought only in his dreams, as we could tell by his actions while asleep.

He was buried with pomp and circumstance on our place; and then there was Casey. . . . But you go and get your own dog and then you'll understand something of how the surgeon feels who does experimental work. If animal lovers knew it, he is the last person they need fear.

10

THE BROTHERHOOD OF MEDICINE

ONE MORNING A FEW YEARS BACK THE MEMBERS OF MY surgical group at the Hopkins made a request to visit a hospital for negroes. It so happened that we had before us a middle-aged, pleasant-spoken, intelligent negro who couldn't be admitted to the Hopkins Hospital because all beds for coloured men were occupied. That wasn't an unusual happening, so, following custom, I suggested another hospital.

"I'm sorry we can't take you, but you have only a simple rupture, and rather than wait a couple of weeks I'd go somewhere else. How about the City Hospital?"

The man looked crestfallen and didn't reply.

"The City Hospital is quite good, you know. Lots of our men are on its staff."

"Well—that is——" he hesitated, "some of us folks don't like those places."

The students standing about smiled, knowing well the antipathy people have to city institutions. Rightly or wrongly, they have an idea that entrance therein carries a stigma and lowers one in the social scale. The aura of the old poorhouse still clings and the idea of accepting municipal charity grates. Private aid is different.

"What would you say to the Provident Hospital? Ever hear of the Provident?" I was following the usual routine, with nothing special in mind. Hospitals owe an obligation to people who come to them for help and one way or another a serious effort is generally made to take care of them.

The man sat there thinking. Finally he looked up and said: "Do you think it's O.K.?"

"Certainly," I replied. "And I should know. I've been there many times."

Then it suddenly occurred to me to tell the students about the place—its story, the thought that gave rise to it, the man responsible. They hear so little of extraneous things during their medical course, and the social element in human relations, the one thing that ought to be poured out to them, is totally lacking. You hear it said that there isn't time, students are overworked as it is, medicine has become too complicated and has gone scientific to such an extent that it takes every ounce of a man's strength and mental prowess to understand it. No one takes account of the undeniable fact that our social relations have undergone equal if not greater change and that to ignore this change only puts off the reckoning. This was an opportunity to open up one small vista to the gaze of a few who needed it sorely—even though they were too young to know it.

"We have in this city," I said, "one of the few hospitals in the country run by coloured people for coloured people exclusively and staffed and nursed by them. It isn't very big—hardly has 150 beds—and it's a comparative newcomer, but it's good. Big things are expected of it and in ways you'd never think of. Like to hear about it?"

My students were interested.

So I told them about the Provident, which is more than a hospital "for the negroes, by the negroes," since its reason for being goes far beyond the care of the sick. It is a training centre for recently graduated negro doctors who hitherto had no such opportunity, or only to such a limited and unsatisfactory extent as to make it negligible.

"How about their medical schools?" asked one of the men.

I was coming to that. They have been few and none too good until recent times. I need hardly mention that with few exceptions negroes are not admitted to our regular medical schools. To help meet the situation at least in part, certain belated schools have been organised for negroes, one of the best being Howard University in Washington. I went over there once with Dr. Finney, who was invited to give an operative clinic. The resident surgeon was Dr. Finney's first assistant and I was his second. When it came to the closure and Dr. Finney stepped away from the table to talk more intimately with the audience, the resident took over and I assisted him. Nothing more, nothing less, the usual routine—except that he was darned good and did a better closure than I could have done.

We remained for lunch and spent an hour or two afterwards looking the place over, meeting various members of the staff, inspecting their work and listening to their comments. Students swarmed over the place, classes and clinics were in full swing, workers were busily engaged in clinical and research laboratories, equipment was first class; in short Howard University was functioning as a university should, and its morale was high.

That was some years ago. It may have been this visit, or perhaps some others, that first gave Dr. Finney the idea for organising the present Provident Hospital in Baltimore. His idea was that while it should have supervision by staff men from the Hopkins and the University of Maryland, these doctors should act chiefly in an advisory and consultative capacity and as instructors, leaving the actual medical and surgical work, as far as possible, in the hands of the resident and visiting staff, all of whom were to be negroes. It took time to gather the staff, because there weren't many recent negro graduates in medicine, and for the most part they all had to come from outside the city, but the opportunity was great and they did come gradually. The hospital also established a training school for nurses. Dr. Finney's plan worked out well. Baltimore now has a nucleus of well-trained negro physicians and surgeons, and the nurses and hospitals to go with them.

The students seemed interested. One of them asked: "Do you think we could visit the Provident, doctor?"

"I could arrange it all right," I said. "Only a couple of weeks ago the resident and I did an amputation together. We're good friends and I've no doubt they'd be glad to do me a favour." About ten days later I took my group of some twenty Hopkins students across town to the Provident. Stopping in front of the old, undistinguished-looking red-brick building I said to them: "This is not to be just a superficial view of another hospital. The superintendent has suggested that I make rounds with you and the hospital personnel, and that is what I propose to do."

For two solid hours, starting with the operating-rooms, supply and sterilising-rooms, all equipped with the most modern apparatus, even to the lights above the operating tables, we went from ward to ward and floor to floor. The place was spotless; every chart was up to date and in place. The nurses and operating-room attachés were carrying on with the quiet competence that one would expect in any well-operated hospital.

In the children's ward was a tot who had fallen out of a window and for a time showed symptoms of a fractured skull. We discussed the symptoms, and the house officer brought out X-rays and gave us the laboratory findings in the same meticulous manner we would have expected at the Hopkins.

On a lower floor were attractive private rooms, some occupied, some not, furnished with the usual paraphernalia of a hospital sickroom. At the end of the hall was the clinical laboratory, and while we were inspecting it I noted two of the students engaged in conversation with a house officer, while another was looking through his microscope. Later on one of the girls walked over and joined in.

On another hall we visited the women's ward, where we came across a young woman whom we had seen in class some two weeks earlier. She had had an abdominal condition and was coming along very nicely after operation. In the men's ward on a lower floor we met our erstwhile friend with the hernia, now operated on and doing well. But there was, I thought, a preponderance of accident cases and I had particular interest in several gunshot wounds. I had been through that ward myself with the resident staff some three or four weeks earlier and remembered one man who was there at that time. He had a shattered leg and there was a question of saving it. He had lost a lot of blood and, among other things, I had suggested a blood transfusion.

We had quite a time over that case. I quizzed students and doctors alike at considerable length. Charts were brought out, X-rays were shown and discussed, blood studies had been made, but no transfusion had been done.

When I asked why, the resident told me that they were having trouble getting blood at the Provident. "Somehow," he said, "our people don't like to give their blood the way others do."

That was something new to me, and I asked him how they explained it.

"We don't explain it entirely," he said, "except that relatives and friends of patients come in and occasionally one of them gives his blood, but the others refuse, even though the need is great and sometimes urgent. They are not entirely conditioned to having their blood taken from them. I guess it's never been put up to them properly."

I inquired if he had asked the Red Cross to take the matter up.

"No," he replied, "we haven't."

Whereupon I told him that I'd look into it myself. And I did later on. My idea was not that the Red Cross should supply the Provident Hospital with blood, but that they should take an interest and perhaps give the instruction and encouragement needed for the hospital to establish a blood bank of its own. The Red Cross promised and some effort was made, but at this writing the Provident still has no blood bank.

After we had said pleasant good-byes to the superintendent and the staff and had crossed the street for our return to the Hopkins, I had a fine idea. "You girls and boys must be tired and hungry—and maybe thirsty! Come on downtown with me to a little place I know and we'll all have dinner together. There's so much that we have to talk over."

It had been a satisfying experience, nothing startling or brilliant, although perhaps a bit unusual, but it had been an illustration of the brotherhood of medicine.

11

SURGEONS GO STALE

NEARLY EVERYBODY GOES STALE SOMETIMES. I KNOW I DO, AND it's not funny. It usually comes after a long stretch of intensive application, and, oddly enough, I rarely realise it myself. It's like being jaundiced. Somebody has to tell me, and generally it's my wife. When she says I've been carrying on long enough and neither the children nor anyone else, herself included, can stand me and my shenanigans any longer, I know that I need a vacation.

"And what's more," she adds, "Miss Gywn says you haven't been exactly an angel around the office!"

"What does she know about it?" I protest irritably.

"Plenty. She says one or two of your operative cases have gone sour and——"

That brings me up sharp. "It's more than one or two," I confess. "Darnedest thing about operative work. Fellow goes along weeks and weeks and everything's hunky-dory, little cases and big cases, easy and hard ones, and then along comes one that goes to pot and the whole caboodle does likewise. And for no good reason. Gosh, but I've been sweating it out these last several weeks. First that little Mrs. Parker who had a simple appendix and got a phlebitis. And then John Dawson's hernia got infected. Did that burn me! I'd told him it was all so easy and simple and he'd be hospitalised only two weeks. It's three now and—and—oh, yes, the little Mason boy's been kicking up something terrible. Empyema case."

But a vacation is never easily or simply come by. You can't just pick up and leave, not if you're a doctor in private practice. People pay you to attend them or operate on them and they have confidence in you and expect you to see them through their ills. Moreover, it's the post-operative stage in surgery that is often most important. People don't always know it, but house officers and nurses do, and no self-respecting surgeon ever thinks of shirking his duty. Just a word, a suggestion maybe, a change of position, sedatives at the right time, withholding one thing and giving another, intravenous glucose maybe a little blood; its surprising to what extent the "know-how" counts in the aggregate, how often the man of experience and judgment relieves anxiety, bucks up patients and attendants, and saves the day when all seems lost.

"We're going away, Miss Gwyn," I said. "Make no appointments after the fifteenth."

I didn't miss her smile, but chose to ignore it.

"Shall I notify the hospitals?"

"Yes, and tell Otley at Quigley I won't operate after the tenth—private or service case—and give Eggers at Fitch Memorial the same message."

"Yes, doctor. I dare say you'll leave young Dr. Caldwell in charge as usual?" The secretary knew the ropes. She made notes and posed other questions, but I had to leave and didn't show up again until the next day, at which time she reminded me of a note coming due—the one on the house we'd built.

"You pay it," I said. "That is, if there's money enough in the account. If not——"

"Oh, there will be," she replied. "I'll send out bills right away and somebody will surely pay up. And that reminds me," she added, "Dr. Ehrich wants to know if you couldn't operate on a patient of his on the twelfth."

"Absolutely not. Tenth is the deadline."

"Just as a favour to him, he said."

"No! No favours. If I operate one day and leave a couple of days later I'll be worried and that'll ruin my golf game."

"I told him all that, but he insisted. I told him he'd have to talk to you personally."

"Damn!"

"And Mrs. Gardner says she can't possibly get her affairs in shape before the fifteenth. Actually wanted to know if your train didn't leave in the afternoon."

"Well, she can go to—— but—let me see. Her husband, Mike, has quite a wad, hasn't he?"

"Rumour has it that way."

"And he's good pay, too. You know what, Miss Gwyn, this thing of doctors going on vacation isn't what it's cracked up to be. Income stops completely, not only while we are away, but several days in advance and several days after we get back. It's a gyp."

"I've often thought of it," the girl said.

"You call up Dr. Fort and say that I insist on Mrs. Gardner getting into the hospital as per schedule or I won't operate on her. I'm damned if I'll lose that fee, and if she's stubborn I'll get in touch with her old man myself."

"Yes, doctor. By the way, how's the little Mason boy doing?"

"Not so good and I hate like thunder to leave him. He came in so late and was so thin and puny. Had a chest full of pus and——"

"His mother's been calling up. She seems worried."

"She hasn't anything on me. I'd feel better about it if

I had more confidence in his doctor. He's so damn cock-
sure and—and unconcerned. Got ice-water in his veins, I
guess. Think I'll make him call in old Brad. Yes, that's
what I'll do and this very day."

Doctors have a habit of talking confidentially to their
secretaries and using them as sounding boards, and, if the
truth be known, doctors' secretaries have a way of suggesting things without seeming to and putting ideas into their
bosses' heads. Helen Gwyn knew I was perturbed about
the Mason boy and she also knew I didn't like his doctor,
the pompous Dr. Ashley. He was so damn up-stage and
all because he had so many big, rich patients. I often wondered what they saw in him. In the four or five cases we'd
had together things had gone fairly well, but when a doctor
has an ego like Ashley's he just can't have consultations
gracefully. I found it out once and had to get Bradley to
help me on the q.t., but other men hadn't been so fortunate. This time I meant to take no chances because the
boy's life depended on it—and so did my vacation.

"You amaze me, doctor," Ashley said when, an hour
later, I remarked that I didn't like the look of Terry.
"Nothing's wrong with the boy that time, good food and
good nursing won't cure."

"But time has a way of running out, Ashley, and the
boy's pulse is jumping around too much to suit me."

"Oh, come now. You're too apprehensive. Terry's
always been nervous."

"Nevertheless," I persisted, "I don't like it and with the
drainage apparently O.K. and the temperature falling and
then shooting up, together with his looks and the pulse——
What do you say to having Chuck Bradley see him with
you? You know Chuck."

"I do, but——"

I wasn't exactly a beginner and knew better than to let the doctor get launched on his usual long-winded objections—as I had the other time.

"Suppose I call him up for you and we meet him here together?" I said.

"But it's so silly, and——"

"How'd three this afternoon suit you?"

"O.K. Only——"

"See you then." And with a wave of the hand I hurriedly slipped away, leaving a red-faced, angry physician standing there in the hospital hall vowing (as I knew well) that he'd never hand me another case, so help him God! That's a way physicians have of punishing refractory surgeons. He didn't, either—not for long months—and the fact that Chuck Bradley diagnosed a purulent pericarditis (pus in the sac around the heart) and that I promptly opened and drained it, and thereby gave the boy a chance, didn't make him any friendlier.

It didn't increase my good humour, either, because it was touch and go with Terry for several days, and though young Dr. Caldwell was perfectly competent to look after the boy and eager to do so, I couldn't bring myself to leave. It was the twentieth before I felt free even to talk about going, and by that time others beside Terry had got on my anxious list.

I was really tired—more than I liked to admit—and there had been collusion between home and office. My wife hadn't liked our not getting away on schedule, but she'd realised the impossibility of my leaving the Mason boy. If I'd left and the boy had died I would never have forgiven myself and the vacation would have been spoiled, whereas if I stayed and even so the boy had died, I would have had the comfort of a clear conscience and could go vacationing with a light heart—or at least one that would soon forget.

Finally, after Gwyn had talked to Dr. Caldwell and reported to my wife that there was no earthly reason why I should not go at any time, she set her lips and got the reservations. We did rest. With the sun and the wind of the mountain resort and a nap in the afternoon, full nights' sleep without one phone call, the jumpy nerves and short temper disappeared and I learned how to laugh and joke again. It didn't even matter to me that almost everyone we met trotted out his, or more likely her, little ills and operations the moment it was discovered I was a doctor. Sometimes it irked my wife. "Why can't they keep their trouble to themselves?" she'd ask. "And why can't they see you are on vacation?" But I reminded her that people are proud of their operations. So another vacation slipped by. On our last evening at the lovely mountain resort I sat on the wide veranda looking at the view for the last time. The clear, starry night, the tang in the air, the quiet —all induced the nostalgia that comes over me with every leave-taking.

But at the same time it was going to be terribly exciting to get back. If I tell you that the urge to operate rises like a gorge, I hope you won't misunderstand. A man is not a surgeon if he doesn't operate: however stale he was when he went on vacation, however much patients and their complaints, and even operating, have got on his nerves, if an overpowering urge for the "feel of the knife" isn't present by the time he gets home, something is seriously wrong. Either the vacation hasn't been long enough or he hasn't the soul of a surgeon. Of the two, I think the latter is the worse because it's something that can't be overcome.

Secretaries and house officers recognise this urge and sometimes go far to provide cases, even to the point of saving them up, and the greater their success the more they smile and are pleased with themselves when the doctor comes back.

"Dr. Willis has two cases for you to do," said Miss Gwyn almost before I'd hung up my hat, "and one is already in the hospital—a stomach." Her face was wreathed in smiles.

"Bully!" I said.

"And Mrs. DeForest wants you to see little Jimmy. His camp doctor says he has an appendix."

"Today?"

"If possible. Dr. Talbot wants to talk to you, too. His boy also has an appendix."

She looked at her notes.

"And, oh, yes, Dr. Graham sent a patient to Quigley yesterday. No diagnosis. And Dr. Williams is sending one in today, and——"

"Wait a minute, sister. Golly!"

"Oh, that's not half," the secretary remarked, smiling, "but I guess you'll want to talk to the boys at the hospital."

"I certainly do." And with that the wheels really did begin to turn. Within the hour at Quigley a man had been brought in with a gunshot wound in the abdomen. His wife who had done the shooting was there with him, demanding private room and private nurses and offering her blood. Police wanted to take her away, but . . . And they had other things for me.

Otley, the resident, was at the door waiting for me.

"Golly, it's good to have you back," he said, shaking hands. "Have a good summer?"

"Yes, bully. And from the looks of things my work's cut out for me."

He laughed. "Well—we have a few little items saved up, but I wonder if you wouldn't like first to take a squint at this gunshot thing. He's in shock and Johnny Floyd's transfusing him, but his wife's the real problem at the moment. Can't quite make her out."

I couldn't, either, at first. The rather tall, middle-aged, nicely dressed but rather dishevelled and distraught-looking woman, who was still hovering about the recovery-room in the accident department, burst out crying when Otley introduced me.

"Oh, doctor," she wailed, "this is all a mistake and you must save my husband."

"We'll do everything possible, madam, but——"

"And don't let the police take me away, please——"

"I haven't anything to do with that," I said. "Now, try to compose yourself and let me go take a look. Perhaps——" And with that I had her led away by a nurse and proceeded to see what could be done. There wasn't much because the bullet had penetrated the upper mid-left abdomen; from the pallor, the pulse, the low blood pressure, and so on, the surmise that a major blood vessel had been injured seemed justified.

No doubt his stomach, too, and maybe something else, I thought, but at the moment there was nothing to do but try to pull him back out of shock. If he came around we would operate, but his chances were none too good.

We never did quite get the low-down on that affair. I told the police that the man would most likely die and persuaded them to let his wife remain at the hospital. Then I sought her out in the room she had engaged and told her the truth as gently as possible.

"These abdominal wounds are extremely serious," I said, "and at the moment it is impossible even to think of operating."

"Oh, but you will, won't you?"

"If the patient comes out of shock, yes, but——"

"Oh, God! if he hadn't taunted me so!"

I turned to go, but she stopped me.

"Wait a minute, doctor, and let me tell you——"

"But, madam, it isn't my affair——"

"Oh, but please," she cried, and I didn't have the heart to leave. Besides, I was somewhat intrigued; and so was young Otley. As we sat on the edge of the bed, I noticed that the hall nurse who had accompanied us didn't leave, either; she was standing just inside the door.

"Mr. Snively and I," the woman proceeded, "have been married fifteen years and have no children. I never was able to conceive, although doctors told me they could discover no reason."

"Did Mr. Snively have himself——" I started to say, and then reconsidered. Fortunately the woman didn't hear me.

"It preyed on Mr. Snively's mind and often he taunted me. Oh, God!" And with that she began walking up and down the room, wringing her hands. "Then there was another woman and—and this morning we had it out. I don't remember where the gun came from, honestly I don't, except that suddenly he had it in his hand and—and—but surely he wasn't going to kill me, now was he?" And with that she halted right in front of me. "Was he, doctor?" she cried.

"Really, madam, I——"

"There was a struggle——"

* * * * *

"There's always a struggle, Otley," I said as we walked away. Sounds to me as if the Mister somehow wasn't smart and came out second best. He might have been the one who was sterile."

"Then she wasn't smart, either," was Otley's observation, and we let it go at that.

I didn't wait for the badly injured patient to snap out of it, for a hospital's routine doesn't stop.

"Well, how are things generally?" I asked Otley.

"Not bad. We've got seven lovely cases saved up for you."

"Really? Now I call that nice." And I did. I'd never once told them to do it; no boss does. It's a sort of unwritten law or custom in the better-run hospitals; the type and number of cases so held over constitute a measure of a man's stature.

"What are they?" I asked.

"Well, sir, we thought you'd like to begin slowly and so there are a couple of breasts scheduled for tomorrow—they came in two days ago—and after that we have two stomachs, a gall-bladder, and a goitre. And Dr. Wiley has something extra special he wants you to see—a lovely aneurism of the femoral." Otley's use of the word "lovely" to describe operative cases was unique with him. Most of the other fellows used the term "bully" or "humdinger" or just plain "good", by which they meant a type of case that would make an interesting, exciting operation, one that any surgeon would have extreme pleasure in doing.

"You're sure these are all nice, easy cases and not things nobody else wanted?"

"We-ll," said Otley with a wide grin, "I have to be honest and tell you that one of the stomachs and one of the goitres have been purposely left for you. But the breasts are easy," he added quickly. "I could do them myself, and Dr. Burton thought they'd do for you to sort of tune up and get your hand in." Burton was one of my devoted younger associates, and I knew well he was showing me high courtesy.

"What have you got in your wards and how are your own personal cases doing? Got any troubles?"

"Who hasn't?" replied Otley. "I did a hernia that got infected, might as well confess it, though nothing else did then or afterwards. And a ruptured appendix obstructed, and, oh, yes, right now there's the nicest old lady whose jaundice won't clear."

"Did you get all her stones?"

"We thought we did, but most likely we didn't."

"What do you say we go have a look?"

For over two hours I oriented myself on the wards by going from bed to bed, scanning every chart, making inquiries and suggestions, doing an occasional dressing to see the condition of suspicious wounds, and finally gathering the whole staff about me for an impromptu conference. Word had gone around the hospital that I was on the wards and every man who could leave what he was doing dropped it and hurried to join me. So, too, did the head nurses, laboratory chiefs, and staff men who happened to be in the house on their own visits. I guess it's like a business whose head has returned. You can feel the pulse of the place grow stronger the moment he takes again and there is an indefinable but definite lift to the morale. To look into the young, eager faces of the staff again, to shake hands with them, as in twos and threes they came along, was to me a great and satisfying pleasure.

"Guess you left a stone down in the lady's common duct, Otley," I said, "and if it wasn't in the ampulla [common duct's mouth] it's there now." We were in the corridor talking.

"Looks like it, sir."

"But I wouldn't worry too much," I went on. "The only fellow who never left a stone is the one who never tried to get them out. But it's tough on the patient. If you'd like I'll assist you at a second trial."

"I was hoping you would," Otley said.

"But you'll do the operating. Once a man starts a job, he's got to finish it or he'll never be a surgeon. I'll be opposite you for luck."

The group was all smiles.

"Hi, Vic," I cried as a tall, slender, grey-haired man came along. "What are you doing in these surgical wards?"

"Oh," said Dr. Bellows, chief of the medical side, smiling, "I just heard you were back and thought I'd drop over to say hello and see if you still know anything about surgery."

"Well, don't stay too long or look too close or you'll find me out."

We chatted, but not for long. Just one or two hospital problems. Afterwards I went to take a look at some of my new patients in the private pavilion, expecting to do the fellow with the bullet-hole in his abdomen if he had come around.

He did come around, but not till after I had seen my private patients and was having lunch. He wasn't doing well even then, but Bellows had seen him, and one or two others, and we thought it was then or never. They said he had regained consciousness and asked for his wife, and in the presence of the police insisted that it was all an accident and his wife was in no way to blame. I wasn't there, but felt awfully good about it when they told me.

The bullet had gone through the stomach and I repaired the two holes—one in the front wall and one in the back wall—but it had also got his left kidney, and that was too much for him. He died next day and nothing happened to his wife—legally, that is!

I was tired that evening and went to bed early with a detective story in order to be in shape for the real stuff next day.

"This is an early scirrhus," I remarked to the group as we got going on the first breast, "but early or late you've got to do a radical, and it's got to be done with care. Mustn't overlook the high axillary glands, and I like to strip the blood vessels."

There was quiet as the work went on, and I admit that I felt much satisfaction at being back in harness.

"Catch this vessel, Otley," I said, "and pick up that one, too. That's good. Might as well have as little bleeding as possible. Golly, it's good to feel a knife again." Otley and the other men who comprised the team were working almost as one man—one man with a flock of hands that seemed never to get in each other's way, but were always where they were needed at the right time. It was beautiful to watch.

"I dare say everything's relative, at that," I remarked a little later. "Only, few people understand how a surgeon can enjoy operating."

We all changed gowns and gloves and with little delay moved into the other operating-room to do the second breast. The several men looking on followed, and an hour or so later, when that case was finished, moved back to Operating Room No. 1 and saw the first stomach done. Afterwards we adjourned for lunch and a little talk and were just about ready for stomach No. 2 when the ambulance brought in an accident case that was so interesting I decided to put off the stomach and make a few observations myself. A little girl of five had pulled a bookcase over on herself in a local department store and complained of pain in the upper right abdomen. Her mother insisted that she had been knocked unconscious, but if so, it must have been momentary because the clerks said the child got up and walked around—until she suddenly vomited. In this instance I thought the usual hospital routine might well stop, chiefly for the benefit of the young house officers.

"I wouldn't be surprised if she has a ruptured liver," I said to Otley, "and if she has we'd better not be tied up with some prolonged, tedious operation we couldn't get out of quickly."

"But Dr. Burton could do her," said Otley.

"How about yourself? Wouldn't you like to have a go at it?"

"Yes, but——"

"There's always got to be a first, son, and we'll do her together."

We did, two hours later, but not until Bellows of the medical staff had been called in consultation. The child was never in serious shock, but she was pale and her pulse was well up. She was somewhat sensitive over the liver area, but not exquisitely so, and X-rays were negative. Signs and symptoms of injury to the kidney were absent; in fact there wasn't a great deal one could put one's finger on. Blood studies were non-committal.

This was the type of case, I told the boys, that required judgment. It was more than likely there was some intra-abdominal bleeding and there could be a ruptured gut. Bleeding can be concealed and, while it may be of little consequence at first, it can suddenly start up and be disastrous. Surgeons, like physicians, try to make absolute diagnosis before operation, but that isn't always possible, nor is it necessary, especially in acute emergencies where the prime thing is to decide whether to operate or not, and if so, when. The child was holding her own fairly well, but she was getting more fretful, and Dr. Bellows and I were of the opinion that it was safest to go in.

All we found was a small, rather superficial tear in the liver. Otley did a bang-up job. With me as his first assistant, he approximated the torn edges with a couple of well-placed stitches—thus effectually stopping the mild blood seepage—covered it with a tag of omentum, and out we came. The child made a nice recovery.

"We'll do that second stomach tomorrow, Otley," I said at the conclusion of the child's operation, "and those other cases, if we get time. Later on we'll tackle your lady with the gallstones. I'm tired now and a fellow shouldn't operate on big things if he's in that fix. Guess I'm still a bit soft."

And there you have it. I don't know if it takes time for the business man to get back in harness after his vacation, but it does for some surgeons. They are soft, or maybe just not conditioned to their arduous work. One of my friends insisted it was too much golf on my part, but how was he to know? He was only a poor physician, and all he did was fish.

12

THE CUSTOMER IS ALWAYS RIGHT

"THE CUSTOMER IS ALWAYS RIGHT." STORES, BIG AND LITTLE, advertise: "Bring your purchases back if you don't like them and we'll exchange them or give you your money back without question." They wouldn't continue the practice if it didn't pay, because they know well the customer isn't always right—so does the customer.

It's different with surgeons. We can't agree that the customer is right when we think he isn't. Furthermore, there's no such thing as exchange of goods in our work—once an operation is done, it's done. Yet the problem of the home-made diagnosis, people's ideas of their own ills, is very real, and the doctor who isn't at times harassed by it simply has no patients. Search your own history and see if some time you haven't had a symptom that said "tuberculosis" to your mind—or was it "appendicitis?"—one that promptly and inexplicably panicked you into calling your doctor post-haste, and fighting it out with him when he didn't agree with you. If you haven't, you are one of the few.

We are able to straighten out the majority of such "customers"—some more easily than others—but certain ones refuse to be budged. Doctors everywhere are constantly seeing and wrestling with such patients and too often coming out second best. I grant that the psychological aspect looms large in the problem; sex and love and marital relations—even business and business worries —are inextricably linked up with it. But when you are faced with a wild-eyed woman who has pains all through her stomach and demands instant operation, or with a pale and drawn man who is sure he has coronary heart disease because of a pounding in his ears and pain in his left chest, you can't just say: "Oh, we'll send you to a psycho-analyst and he'll set you right."

In the first place there wouldn't be enough psycho-analysts; in the second place your patients wouldn't go to one if there were; in the third place they'd throw you out and get another doctor; in the fourth place they could be right and sometimes are! If you are a doctor you might as well make up your mind that you are going to have some patients of this kind, and you'd better learn how to deal with them. I can't speak for the physicians and don't pretend to, but it is a fact that great numbers of these patients present combined medico-surgical problems that demand the highest talents and try the souls of surgeons and physicians alike.

Consider the famous major-league baseball player who had his appendix removed during the late winter some years ago and went into spring training too soon. Every time he threw a ball, every time he swung a bat, he got a stitch in his right side. Someone told him it was due to adhesions and would soon pass off, but instead of being comforted he became more worried than ever. Loss of sleep, loss of appetite, loss of weight followed in quick succession; a cough developed and presto! his disordered mind seized upon tuberculosis as the cause. The club physician, the family physician, the local specialist, no one could convince the great man that his own diagnosis was wrong. We couldn't, either, when he came to Baltimore, but somehow we didn't seem to care much, and that shocked him to the core.

E*

"Tell you what, my friend," I said to him in a rather off-hand manner after he had been with us two days, "you go on into the hospital and get a good long rest, and while you're there I'll have some more studies made and we'll really see. Dr. Roberts says he can't find any tuberculosis and Dr. Kinney says the X-rays are negative, but they could be wrong, and we'll make further studies."

"But—but——" the ball player started to say.

"But what, son?"

"I was about to say," he went on, "that the season will be opening soon, and here you want to put me in a hospital and—and you don't seem worried, but it's my whole future."

I couldn't help laughing, he was so comical looking, this lithe young fellow with the deep chest and broad shoulders. I didn't wonder that he had great baseball ability or that he was used to having people take him and his health seriously.

"We-ll," I drawled, "I don't think your future is in great danger. You've got yourself all tied up into a knot and——"

"But tuberculosis is no knot to my way of thinking," he broke in, "and neither are adhesions. They say you can cut adhesions loose, and if I haven't tuberculosis why not cut them and be done with it so I can get back into the game?"

We had a terrible time with the man. It finally devolved that it was his failure to hit that had really put him on the rocks. In addition to being a fleet-footed out-fielder he had been a fine hitter—timely and dangerous in the clutches—and when that went off, even in early pre-season practise, because of the sudden stitch in his side when he struck at the ball, bang went his confidence. His whole world collapsed. He lost seventeen pounds, his whole demeanour changed, there was no living with him, he was to all intents and purposes a dead duck so far as baseball was concerned, and tuberculosis or adhesions or both were engraved on his mind.

He did have a bad pair of tonsils which we removed, but other than that, all we gave him was a prolonged rest in bed with forced feeding and an occasional pep talk. It may be that removal of the tonsils helped some, but his nervous cough gradually disappeared, he forgot about his adhesions, regained most of his weight and even talked pleasantly to his long-suffering wife. He did worry about not opening the season in his accustomed place, but we were adamant and finally convinced him that if he didn't listen to us his future would be blasted. What we feared most was a relapse if he went back to playing and still found his batting not up to standard—pain in the side or no pain. I was an old baseball player myself and knew well how disastrous that could be. I felt sure that he'd be able to run and field as of old—somehow or other that is easier —but hitting is something else again, and nothing disturbs a player more than a slump in this department.

So I wrote his manager and got intelligent co-operation. The player was sent home, but was permitted only to watch games—and from the grand-stand. Under no circumstances was he to put on a uniform and sit on the bench during the first week and under no circumstances was he to engage in practice. He was to eat and sleep and get conditioned to being with professional ball players and talking their lingo. Following that he was to practise everything but batting, slowly, gradually, for one week. Then batting was to be included. Manager and player followed directions implicitly, and it is a pleasure to relate that by mid-season one of America's great baseball heroes was again gracing the headlines. For several years thereafter—until age finally did him in—he continued to perform prodigious feats at bat as well as in the field.

Not so good was the result obtained in the patient who had an obvious breast cancer but refused operation because she didn't wish to be disfigured. That is an understandable objection and one not infrequently encountered.

"Can't you do something for me, doctor, other than operate?" the patient asked.

"X-ray would be the only treatment I know of that might hold out hope," I replied. "But I don't advise it in the first place, and in the second place you've already delayed, and operation is your best bet."

"But I still think doctors ought to be able to do something besides operate."

"I take it," I said, "that you do not dispute the diagnosis?"

"No," she admitted blandly. "I've consulted other doctors and you all seem to agree."

We had a long conference, but I couldn't bring her to my viewpoint and she left. I didn't see her again for perhaps three months, at which time she returned with the story that she'd shopped around still further and had found a doctor who had been giving her injections by needle of a cancer cure of his own.

"With what results?" I asked.

"We-ll——"

"Would you mind letting me see?"

She did rather reluctantly and there was no doubt of advancement.

"Are you going to continue with the injections," I asked, "or will you now come in for a belated operation?"

"It's the disfigurement, doctor," she replied, "and I cannot bring myself to go through with it." Her eyes were moist but she did not cry. She was a woman in her middle forties, quite youthful looking and attractive, married and the mother of two children. Her husband could do nothing with her nor could anybody else. I did my best, but she continued with the injections until pain and a tumour that could no longer be denied drove her to operation by another surgeon—too late. Since, however, death did not occur for another two years, it was obvious that she had a cancer of low-grade activity and might well have had a permanent cure.

The doctor who had experimented on her? Oh, nothing happened to him. It never does.

We had better luck with another woman who was equally adamant, only this time the objection was to the usual post-operative treatment. This opinionated, self-willed person who made no bones about disliking doctors and "all their silly notions and medicines" had come to operation because of a pelvic tumour. We all hoped she'd stage a good recovery, but she had rough going afterwards. There she was, forty-eight hours after the operation, all blown up and nauseated and acting as if she had an intestinal obstruction. When she got to vomiting and became dehydrated and refused all medication by mouth or otherwise—even including fluid by veins—things first got tense and then desperate.

To my pleadings she only shook her head and said, almost in a whisper: "I do not believe in medicines, and your treatments will only make me worse."

"But just let us try this once."

"No, and if you attempt to force that tube——"

"We won't force anything, but you must see that we cannot be responsible for——"

"I will pray," was all she said, and that was that.

I cannot say whether it was the efficacy of prayer or not, but just about that time a young assistant resident who had been in on the case came along and suggested that we turn the lady flat on her stomach and then tilt the foot end of the bed well up so that her head would be very low.

"I know she's badly distended," he said, "and it's bound to be uncomfortable, but what have we got to lose?"

"Not much at that," I replied, "but the nurses have turned her from side to side several times and quite without results. That's almost as good as turning her over flat."

"Yes, sir, it is, but not quite, and besides, her whole body hasn't been slanted down the way I'm suggesting."

We'd been standing to one side of the room talking in low tones so the patient wouldn't hear us, but I couldn't help noticing her suspicious eye.

"Go ahead and try it," I said, "but don't fight her if she objects too seriously. Get in an extra nurse to help you and her special, and be as gentle as you can." And with that I left, convinced that the woman would not co-operate and that little good would come of it even if she did. I really thought she'd die, and told her husband so.

But she didn't die, and the house officer succeeded far beyond his expectations. The patient not only consented to be turned flat over and head down, but had the effrontery to say she'd been wondering why we hadn't thought of it before. *She* had. Within the hour pent-up intestinal fluid and gas began to pour out, there was prompt and complete relief, and in twelve hours the picture had changed completely.

"Didn't I tell you," she said to me next morning, "that my prayers would be answered and no medicines were necessary?"

"Yes, ma'am," I replied, "you certainly did, and my advice to you is to keep on praying till you get out of here."

I didn't miss the look she gave me, or the young resident's grin. She made a perfect recovery and throughout the years never fails to tell me how little the doctors know.

We had another somewhat similar case of a little five-year-old girl who, too, had had an abdominal operation, the result of an accident. She was a pretty little blue-eyed blonde, but, like a lot of other blondes, had a will of her own and successfully frustrated every effort of nurse, doctor, mother, and father to get fluids into her. We didn't want to use the intravenous method because she was so apprehensive and, besides, her veins were so small it wouldn't have been easy. So we played along and were getting nowhere when the mother said: "Doctor, Leila's terribly fond of 7-Up, and if you think——"

"If I think!" I cried. "The time's past for thinking, and if she'll take 7-Up or 7-Down it's all the same so long as it's fluids and sugar. Order a bottle, nurse, or better still, run down and get one and we'll see."

This is no plug for 7-Up, but it is a fact that the moment the child laid eyes on the bottle her face became wreathed in smiles—for the very first time—and she literally gulped the drink. Her recovery was swift and uneventful.

*   *   *   *   *

Of all patients, the most trying are those who have read up on their ills, real or imaginary. And I think their number is growing. What with the medical literature carried nowadays in newspapers and magazines, too much of it written by non-professionals or ghost-written; what with the ease of access to libraries, all of which have some books on medicine; finally, what with the increased interest in medicine and medical affairs generally, it is not unnatural that the sick should be learning more about their ills. Generally speaking, I think it is a good thing, but sometimes it can be disastrous. It's the old story, of course, of a little knowledge being a dangerous thing.

Take the case of the stalwart young man I saw a short time ago. He came in complaining of circulatory disorder in his legs and gave me the diagnosis, quoted authorities, and then, looking me straight in the eyes, practically dared me to contradict him. He was a college graduate, age thirty-two, married to a chronically ill wife, no children, intelligent but very introspective, poor, artist by desire, but not profession because the war and work in munitions and other factories interfered. Mild pain and discomfort in his legs, cold feet, and a local doctor's suggestion that it might be Raynaud's disease rang the bell, and he was off. I feel sure he thought I was a very poor doctor when I told him, after careful examination, that he didn't have any circulatory trouble whatever, much less Raynaud's.

"But I've studied up on the thing and have seen doctors and——"

"That's a good part of your trouble," I broke in. "You've studied too much and misinterpreted things and you've taken doctors too literally."

"But——"

"And more than likely it's the unaccustomed work

you've been doing and the long hours of standing that are at the bottom of your trouble."

"You really think so?" He looked bewildered.

"That, together with worry over your wife, frustration at not being able to go on with your painting, your uncertain future, and things of that sort. Know what you ought to do?"

"What?"

"Take your wife and hop into the old jalopy and go on out to the Middle West where you came from. Get a job as a forester and keep it two years or so, working out of doors all the time and living the simple life. It will do your wife good, too. Forget yourself, breathe the free air once again, get tired, but not too tired, and enjoy your wife's cooking. At the end of two years go on back to painting if it still appeals to you and let nothing dissuade you from it, even if you have to starve."

I don't know whether he took the advice or not, but he said he would, and certainly the dour look on his face had given way to a smile.

Incidentally, he was referred to me by a psycho-analyst.

I had another patient some years back who did have circulatory trouble, and if ever I came out second best, if ever a patient was right, it was in the case of that man. My face is red right now as I write these lines. All I wanted to do was amputate the man's left leg! But he wouldn't hear of it and actually argued the thing out with me—anatomically, pathologically, therapeutically. Oh, I stood my ground and I quoted authorities, but it was his leg, and he quoted authorities just as good as mine. In fact he did better than that. He picked himself up, journeyed to another city, put himself under the care of one of his authorities—and walked in on me six months later under his own two-legged power, grinning from ear to ear. I didn't see anything funny about it.

No operation, big or little, is devoid of danger, and only too often trouble comes when and where you'd least expect it. The conscientious surgeon—and physician—tells that to his patients, but some of them refuse to listen or say: "You're just trying to frighten me."

Not so long ago I saw a woman whose abdomen had so many scars, some of them criss-crossing and looking like Japanese writing, that you couldn't make out where one ended and another began. It all started years back with a gall-bladder that had to be removed. The wound broke open. It healed but a hernia resulted, and that had to be done. Then she obstructed—or said she did—from adhesions and that occasioned further operation. Next came something of a pelvic nature, and—but I couldn't follow her, and if it hadn't been for the tell-tale scars I'd have thought she was making it up. Yet there she was pleading for still another operation—for adhesions.

"I get the worst cramps, doctor," she said, "and I'm convinced its more adhesions."

"But you do get along," I said. "You don't obstruct."

"Oh, no, not completely."

"And you know well," I went on, "that if we did go in and separate the adhesions—a formidable procedure in itself in your case—you'd only have them again, probably worse."

"Yes, of course, but that would be my risk."

Think of it! Think of a person with all that experience of operations asking for more! We refused, of course, and outlined a special regime of diet and treatment for her, but, as I said to the students after she had left: "This patient has operation on the brain and it is my opinion that sooner or later she will prevail on someone to do her. We see cases of this sort every once in a while, and if they don't exactly like operation they do get conditioned to it and do not fear it as others do."

"Would you say people talk themselves into operation, doctor?" asked one young man. "You hear the expression used and I just wondered."

"Well, it is a fact that many people get pleasure out of their hospital experience. *Speaking of Operations* by Irvin Cobb, you may remember, was a very popular book. You've all had to stand by to look at some friend's beautiful scar and listened to the tiresome story of how he almost died after his operation, and the pain was something awful, and if it hadn't been for Old Doc Whosit and his miracles he wouldn't be there to tell it—which would be all right by you, too. It's hard to explain, but some people get a sort of euphoria after their operations, and in their happiness forget, or tend to play down, the unpleasant part. Sometimes I think it's because they were scared half to death and thought in their subconscious they were going to die. The unexpected deliverance touches off the spark of thankfulness, which manifests itself ever afterwards in exhibitionism and an inclination to 'tell the world' at the slightest provocation."

"If it weren't sometimes so tragic I would think it was really funny. There isn't the shadow of a doubt that some women have their imaginations fired by the intimate stories told by their friends and come to operation that isn't always necessary. Men do, too, but to a less extent because they don't sit around bridge tables so much, they don't talk nearly so intimately to each other as women do, they are less gullible, and finally they haven't the courage for operation that women have. Now mind you, I'm only giving you my personal opinion."

And talking oneself into operation does have some basis in fact. I know one young married woman who went to a doctor and a chiropractor for her backache and general feeling of illness, constantly talking of and looking forward to the operation "I just know I'm going to have". Her aches and pains never prevented her from going to dinner-parties, the theatre, playing golf, taking long automobile drives, and dancing at night clubs. She looked the picture of health. But operated on she was, and how she complained when there were days and days of post-operative discomfort, treatments, intravenous therapy, hypodermics, dressings, and all!

"They didn't tell me about those things!" she wailed.

"Who didn't?" I asked.

"The girls. They had the same operation and said it was nothing."

I had to laugh. "Didn't you know it was a major operation?"

"Yes, but——"

"Did you really think you'd get up and walk out of the hospital a few days later, maybe a week—all well and ready to go?"

I could cite other instances. Many people take surgical procedures too lightly, and some doctors do. Our customers are right sometimes but not always. But right or wrong, there's no exchange in surgery and it does little good to return their money—if collected—when the result has not been a success.

13

DOCTOR ABOARD?

"IS THERE A DOCTOR ABOARD? IS THERE A DOCTOR ABOARD?"

It was late at night. As the train conductor slowly made his way through the car, I kept right on reading. After he had passed, a man sitting next to me in the lounge leaned over and said: "What's the matter, doctor? Hiding?"

"Oh, no; that is, not exactly," I replied. "I just like to let the other fellow do his stint. If the conductor doesn't find someone he'll be back and then I'll own up."

The man chuckled but didn't say anything. I didn't know him, but apparently he knew me; doctors are marked men and rarely are able to evade their responsibilities.

"It isn't that I object to giving my professional services when needed," I remarked by way of explanation, "but what with my long years of toil, the war and all, I feel like—well, you know."

"Sounds reasonable enough," he replied, and was about to go on when back came the conductor with the same call, and it was up to me to go.

"What's the matter, conductor?" I asked, rising.

"You a doctor?"

"Yes."

"Well, there's a woman in the sleeper up ahead crying out in pain . . ."

"O.K. Lead the way."

When I returned after some twenty minutes, the man was still there, and he motioned me to the seat next to him.

"What was it?" he asked.

"Oh, nothing much. Dope fiend." I must have sighed, for he remarked that I looked tired.

"I am," I said. "It wasn't a pleasant experience. They're tragic figures. Morphine addicts, I mean. And they're so readable to one who's knocked about a bit. You take that poor soul up ahead, for instance; young, nice-looking woman with a hard face. She was lying doubled up in a lower berth, curtains all back for anyone to see, while several women tried vainly to soothe her, and a few anxious men hovered in the background. When I attempted to get the story she kept pointing to her stomach, crying: 'Here, here. Pain, terrible pain!' That was all the information I could get, and each question seemed to make her writhe more. And she wasn't undressed. That aroused my suspicions. The first thing most women do for abdominal discomfort is loosen the girdle." I took up the story:

" 'When did she get on the train?" I asked the conductor.

" 'About two hours ago and she's got to get off first thing in the morning.'

" 'How long ago did she become ill?'

" 'These ladies say she was apparently O.K. until she started to bed about an hour ago. That's right, isn't it?'

" 'Yes,' replied one of the women, 'and her suffering was intense from the very beginning. She just fell over in her berth and wouldn't even let us touch her, undress her, that is.'

"I turned back to the patient, who had grown a little quieter. 'Madam,' I said, 'would you just let one of these ladies undo your dress so that I can examine you a bit?"

"That set her off worse than ever; she rolled from one side of the berth to the other—in too much agony. They're tough cookies, dope fiends, and will play you until you make a move that tells them you're on to their game—then they collapse. I showed that lady my hand by trying to get a squint at her eyes. I didn't succeed because she jerked her head away, and when I tried again she sat bolt upright and shrieked: 'What in hell are you trying to do, poke my eyes out?"

"What *were* you trying to do, doctor," queried my friend, "besides showing your hand?"

"Well, opium derivatives cause a narrowing of the pupils, excessive, even pin-point, as it is called, and, of course. . ."

"I see."

"But she would have none of it, and when I insisted on examining her abdomen she gave me another blast.

" 'Look here, you,' she cried out, 'if you're such a great doctor why don't you give me something for this pain and be on your way?'

"Leaning over so no one could possibly hear me, but speaking firmly, I asked: 'When did you have your last dose of morphine, and who do you think you're kidding?'

"Instantly the poor soul let out another scream. I don't know what the people around us thought, but I was certain then what the trouble was and I kept right after her.

" 'Now you listen to me,' I said, 'and cut out this monkey business or I'm going to spill the whole business to the conductor and advise him to put you off the train. '

"Why, you black-hearted bastard! You wouldn't dare!'

" 'The hell I wouldn't!' And when I started as if to go, she clutched my arm and wouldn't let me.

" 'Oh, doc, I'm half crazy!' she cried. 'Give me something, won't you? I—I—'

" 'You what?'

" 'Well, to tell the truth I ran out of the stuff and . . .'

"They're the biggest liars, you know. You can't believe a word they say."

"What did you do?" inquired the listener.

"Oh, I gave her a quarter grain and got roundly cursed for it. She wanted a grain and that isn't a big dose for lots of them, but, after all, I didn't know the woman or what she was up to, and one can get in trouble so easily."

"Did you tell the conductor?"

"Yes, I had him come and stand beside me so that both of them would get it clear.

" 'This quarter grain to be taken by mouth will tide you over till morning, young lady,' I said, 'or it can if you are smart. But just in case you take it into your head to put on another show I'm suggesting to the conductor that he put you off the train at the very next stop. I'm also telling him and you, too, not to call me during the night, because I'm not coming.' "

"Kind of tough, isn't it?" remarked my new-found friend, but before I could reply the conductor came up and asked if I would fill out a little slip he had in his hand.

"I have to make out a report on that woman, doctor, and, of course, if you'll put in a claim the railroad will reimburse you for your services."

"Thanks a lot, but doctors don't charge for services like that—at least I don't—and if you don't mind I'd rather not sign anything." Sometimes people get ideas and there's a suit against the railroad and all sorts of trouble. The doctor has to appear, and at the best it takes too much of his time and energy.

I continued: "You just make out your own report and let it go at that—no names mentioned. That is, if it goes no further than this."

He smiled, but looked rather nonplussed.

"O.K.," he said. "Thanks, anyhow, for helping me out. She's calmed down and, I hope, gone to sleep."

And with that my friend and I turned in.

There was another occasion, this time on a big ocean-going luxury liner turned cruise ship. We had all been gay and happy as the ship pulled away from her pier and pointed down New York harbour. To get away from wintry blasts and snow and ice is enough to cheer up anybody, and our group was no exception. It was our first trip to the Caribbean, and I looked forward very eagerly to the prospect of blue skies, smooth seas, and beautiful ports of landing. Even the storm that we ran into eight hours out and the rough seas and general buffeting the ship and all aboard stood for forty-eight hours didn't dampen my enthusiasm—for I was a good sailor.

But it did bother many of the others, among them a man of some fifty years who, it turned out, had come aboard in a wheel-chair. I hadn't seen him myself and knew nothing about his case until Dr. Harris, the ship's doctor, knocked at the door of our cabin on the third morning and asked if he could talk to me.

"Certainly. Come in," I replied.

"I understand from another doctor among the passengers that you're a surgeon," he said.

"That's right."

"Would you mind seeing a case with me and the other doctor? Two doctors, in fact."

"I will be glad to. What's it all about?"

"There is a Mr. Selby down on D-deck who was ill when he came aboard—gastric ulcer—and something's happened to him."

"Why did he start out on such a trip as this when he wasn't well?"

"Doctor's orders, apparently, but that doesn't make sense to me."

"What happened? Do you think the storm did him in?"

"That, too, is a question," the doctor replied. "But more than likely it did, because he got to vomiting and retching shortly after the blow began and nothing that I did helped. He didn't look so good at the beginning and now he looks worse, considerably worse—so bad, in fact, that last night I called in consultation a doctor I knew among the passengers and he got in another one. We are afraid it's something surgical, and since all three of us are physicians, we scanned the passenger list and you happen to be the only surgeon aboard. I've therefore taken the liberty . . ."

It took only a glance to see that the man was desperately ill, and the moment my hand touched his abdomen there was little doubt but that some inner catastrophe had occurred. There was the board-like musculature and the exquisite sensitiveness, more exaggerated over the stomach area, but generally diffuse as well. The patient looked ashen grey, his pulse was rapid and none too good, and he was in dangerous shock. I tried hard to avoid his questioning eyes, but only partially succeeded, and knew well by his complete silence that he read my mind. When his wife, who had been standing in the background seemed about to ask questions, I motioned to her to come outside, where we told her as gently as possible how sick her husband was. She took it better than I thought she would, but her anguish was only partially concealed.

"Have you any relatives or friends aboard?" I asked.

"None," she replied. "We only decided on the trip at the last moment. I don't know a soul on the boat, but three or four passengers with cabins near-by have been awfully kind. Please do what you can to save my husband and—and spare no expense."

"That's not the point, madam. It's . . . Suppose you remain down here with your husband while the ship's doctor and I and the two other doctors talk things over."

She agreed and we left to find the others.

"What do you think, doctor?" asked Harris as we approached the elevator.

"The same as you do—that's it's a hundred to one he dies."

"Think he's got a ruptured gastric ulcer?"

"More than likely; and what's more, it's not recent. For all you know it might have perforated during the first hours of the storm, when he did most of his hard vomiting, and that's thirty-six hours or more ago. That's why he looks so bad. He's got considerable of a peritonitis."

"Think I could have done better by him?"

"He should never have come aboard. That's what I think. What's the first port of landing?"

"Puerto Rico."

"When are we due?"

"Well . . ." But just then we came across the other doctors and the four of us went into a huddle. It wasn't much of a huddle, at that, because we were all of the same mind. This despite the fact that we were complete strangers.

"I'm sorry for the man," Dr. Blake said.

"And his wife," put in Dr. McLane. "What a beating she's taking."

"And will continue to take," added Dr. Harris.

"Yes. But what do you fellows think is the best thing to do, if anything?" I asked.

"That's the point—if anything," said Harris. "Short of a miracle, that man is a dead duck; and miracles don't happen often."

McLane turned to me. "Last night we thought it best to try to carry him along till the ship reaches Puerto Rico, but now——"

"Why don't we get the captain down here and find out just how soon he can get there and put the matter up to him straight? I dare say you've told him?" I asked the ship's doctor.

"Oh, yes, he knows all about it and instructed me to call you gentlemen. If you will wait here I'll try to find him."

To pass the time we discussed the pros and cons of such medical measures as could be invoked—mostly sedatives, ice-bags, nothing by mouth, and so on. I told them frankly I didn't think the man was in any shape to stand operation. When the captain arrived—a big, broad-shouldered, weather-beaten man of about fifty—I told him the same thing, and wound up by asking how soon we could reach Puerto Rico, where there was a good hospital and, among other things, facilities for blood transfusion, which we did not have. Two or three doses of blood would have bucked him up tremendously, and possibly made him a fair operative risk, but this all happened some years back, when ships didn't carry plasma and apparatus for blood transfusion as they do now.

"The storm has delayed us, and even if I pushed the ship we couldn't reach Puerto Rico under thirty-six hours at the earliest," the captain replied. "And since that would be about midnight, I'd have to lay outside till daylight because the channel is too narrow and shallow for a ship of this size to negotiate in the dark."

"That makes nearly two days, then."

"Yes."

"He'll be dead by that time."

"Even if you operate?" asked the captain.

"That's about the only chance, but the odds are much against him."

"What's wrong with him and why couldn't he survive an operation?"

"We think he's got a ruptured stomach ulcer in the first place, and in the second place he is in a state verging on collapse and——" I did my best to explain.

No one spoke for a moment. Finally the captain said: "I think you doctors ought to place the matter frankly before the man's wife and let her decide. I'll go with you."

So down we trooped to D-deck. That lady had courage. Other than asking a question now and then she said nothing throughout the painful recitation and at its conclusion her answer came promptly and without the slightest equivocation.

"I can see my husband dying before my very eyes the way things are going now, and if there's one chance in a thousand by operation, I wish it done."

Turning then to the captain she said: "What would you do if you were in my place?"

"I think I'd take the same position you are taking, madam," he replied. "And, now, if you gentlemen will make such preparations as are needed and let me know the exact time of the operation I'll then decide how best to handle the ship. Dr. Harris and all the ship's company will place everything we have at your disposal."

With that he left us. It wasn't a command, exactly, but it amounted to the same thing and my heart sank. The ship was still rolling a little; the air was dank and moist, and with all port-holes still closed and the ship's engines pounding away in heavy audible crescendo, the outlook was dismal. I walked away from the conference, depression and anxiety were upon me—and silence. The ship's captain had ordained; there was nothing further to discuss. We went about the business of preparation.

There weren't the usual instruments and sterile stuff for a stomach operation, but we gathered up what there was. As luck had it, just before sailing one of the doctors had bought same new clamps for his hospital and had them with him. The ship's sick bay wasn't anything to boast about and, besides, it was on another deck. We had agreed that the man was too ill to be moved. It became necessary, therefore, for carpenters and electricians to rig up special lights and stands in his state-room. Some two or three hours later—just as darkness came on—we notified the captain that all was ready, and he promptly came down for a last consultation. I was accustomed to operating under pretty terrible conditions, what with front-line surgical experience during the war, but this was the first time I had ever performed at sea and in a little state-room at that, with the patient in a bunk that could be approached from one side only. And I was nervous. With the boat rolling and pitching I hoped the rubber tennis shoes my wife had rummaged out of the trunk would at least give me a steady footing.

"I could stop the ship completely during the operation," said the captain, turning to me, "but with the seas still running high the ship would roll much more than she's doing now."

"What else could you do?" I asked.

"I could slow down, change my course, and head her into the wind," he replied. "She'll be steadiest then and I'll hold her there till you've finished."

And that's what he did immediately. We could feel the change as soon as it was made. After I had washed up and put on gown and gloves, and the ship's doctor and McLane had done likewise, Blake started the ether. Two skilled hospital orderlies had brought boiled instruments, gauze, catgut, needles, and so on from the sterilisers, and a ship's nurse stood by to do what she could. The man was so weak it didn't take long to put him to sleep, and to save time I had cleaned his abdominal skin and spread sterile towels in advance. Kneeling, then, beside the bunk and with two high-powered electric lights above my head, I made the incision in the man's upper right abdomen, and in no time was down to the peritoneum. Little bleeding was encountered because of the patient's shock and lowered blood-pressure, so I hurriedly picked that up and opened it—and was literally flooded out by the cloudy, slightly blood-tinged fluid that welled up.

"Looks as though it might be an ulcer, all right," I said, and was just starting to bring the pyloric (lower) end of the stomach into view when the anæsthetist said: "He's doing very badly, doctor; pulse is hardly perceptible."

"Suppose we stop everything for a while and you take the ether off."

"O.K., but he's had very little."

"If I could just get a little peek in there and maybe . . ."

He did pick up a bit, but it was apparent that further manipulations would kill him immediately, so I tucked a couple of drains down towards the pelvis, put in a few through-and-through sutures, and called it a day. Time of operation: hardly ten minutes. Immediately word went to the bridge and we could feel the ship resuming her course. The captain came down from the bridge, thanked us all, said we'd done a fine piece of work under unusually difficult conditions, hoped all would turn out well, even if it didn't look as though it would, and was gone.

We doctors stood there in the tiny cabin, now littered with soiled towels and stained gauze and gowns, talking in hushed tones while orderlies began putting things to rights. I leaned over with my ear almost to the patient's mouth to hear his breathing and only got the very faintest sound.

"His pulse at the wrist here is barely perceptible," said Harris.

"It isn't much better in his temporals," Blake said.

The orderly untied my gown, slipped it off my shoulders, and then helped me take the thin rubber gloves off my hands. He didn't say a word, but I could tell by his helpful efforts that he was sorry, and in the only way possible was trying to comfort me. I couldn't remember when an operation, even a complete and utter failure like this one, had affected me so. With the ship's doctor, I looked up the man's wife, told her as gently as possible of the findings and of the unsatisfactory procedure—and went to my own cabin, unhappy and in a blue funk. The man died some five hours later. A futile effort had been made. The brave wife went ashore at Puerto Rico two days later and took her husband's body with her.

In the weeks that followed I gradually regained my composure and had all but forgotten about the episode—only to have it brought home to me at the pier when we landed in New York. We had hardly got ashore, the inspectors hadn't begun with our baggage when a man stepped up, introduced himself as my patient's brother, wanted to know what my fee was, took out a cheque book, and said: "Doctor, the family wishes to pay you and the other doctors in full for your services and we are very grateful."

"There is no charge," I said. "We did what we could and that was little enough, but there's no charge." The three of us had made up our minds to that.

"But we insist on paying, because we want the complete story, yours in particular, and . . ."

"Now listen to me," I replied. "I did what I could for your brother on that ship, but before operating I exacted from the ship's captain his word that under no circumstances would I assume any responsibility whatever in the case. What you have in mind is a lawsuit, isn't that so?"

"Well . . ."

"Well, I'll be no party to it one way or the other, but I did think of the possibility, and warned both the ship's doctor and the captain that they'd best have a very carefully written report ready by the time we landed. They have that and I presume you can get a copy from them. Thank you, and good-bye."

F

14

COMFORT WHILE YOU WAIT

IT WAS ONE OF THOSE WARM, HUMID DAYS OF MID-AUGUST AND the last thing in the world I wished to do was to escort visitors through the hospital. I wouldn't have done it, either, if it hadn't been that Josh Macklin, an old friend of mine, and his wife were bent on a look before drawing up final plans for the hospital they were giving their little home town in Oklahoma.

They liked the hospital proper a great deal, and were especially impressed with the light and airy wards, the diet kitchens, the well-equipped, clean utility rooms, and the quiet rooms available for the very sick.

"I think it's wonderful," Catherine said, "to be able to spare ward patients the sight and sufferings of the desperately ill and dying. We mustn't forget to incorporate that, Josh."

"We mustn't forget to put in a reading and recreation-rom for ward patients, either," Josh said.

"Would you like to see the laboratories and operating-rooms?" I offered.

"Yes, we'd like to see it all if you don't mind," said Catherine, giving me a pitying and slightly amused smile.

"Oh, I'm terribly pleased," I said, grimacing. So we trudged on through the whole place, stopping occasionally for closer inspection, until finally we reached the admitting-room of the out-patient department.

"What a dismal, depressing place!" Catherine exclaimed. "What did you say this is?"

"This is where people who come in for examination are registered, sorted, and distributed to the various departments—people of all kinds, mostly poor, whites, blacks, women, children, foreigners, everybody."

It was rather late in the afternoon and only a few patients were there. One tired-looking dishevelled woman was nursing her baby; a red-faced man not far from her was dozing; two children, one white and the other black, were playing on the dirty floor while their mothers sat talking; a secretary was typing away.

Catherine had left us and was slowly walking up and down the aisle, peering around, sniffing the air.

"This is the most terrible place I have ever been in," were her first words when I caught up with her. "Those poor people. The very air smells to heaven. And look at those straight-backed, hard, dark-coloured wooden benches. Not a cushion on one of them. How long do people have to sit here?"

"Why——"

"Hours, I guess."

"Yes. Sometimes, I suppose. Till they're seen."

"And they're all sick."

"Most of them." I was beginning to get her drift and it gave me a sickening feeling.

"Artificial light in here, too," she went on. "And none too good. A person couldn't read if he wanted to. Not a drop of sunlight trickles through those dirty windows and they're mostly closed."

Josh had come up by this time, but remained quiet.

"What in the world do these people do while they're waiting?" asked Catherine.

"Nothing, so far as I know." I don't believe I'd ever thought of it before.

"And what about the children? Are they supposed to sit still and keep quiet, too?"

"Yes, but they don't always."

"Now I believe I've seen everything," said Catherine. "Bertie," she asked, swinging around and facing me, "how typical is this of all the waiting-rooms that you've known? How many of them are like this, grim and dirty and thick with the faintly nauseating odour of charity? Is this one particularly awful or are they all alike?"

It was amazing. I had worked and taught in that dispensary for years—yes, and liked it. Now she was throwing a monkey-wrench into it and making it look awful. Furthermore, her words brought to my mind a long procession of waiting-rooms, dingy rooms stuck away in a basement or on a back court, bleak rooms, each one with benches harder than the other, and drearier walls and a more depressing atmosphere. No matter how beautiful and new and modern the hospital is, the waiting-room of the dispensary is as like all others as peas in a pod. Their shapes and furnishings may vary, but practically all of them are permeated with what Catherine called "the faintly nauseating odour of charity." I could remember a few waiting-rooms in children's departments where an effort at cheerfulness had been made, but all in all, now that I could not escape thinking about it, those hospital waiting-rooms were the most dismal and uncomfortable places I could imagine.

Just goes to show, I said to myself as I showered and got ready for dinner. A fellow gets too close to his work. Again I had completely overlooked the fact that sick people need more than medicine. And the psychological effect that a big, dark, dreary, smelly, sometimes overcrowded waiting-room must have on them had escaped me. It shouldn't have, but it had. What it meant to sit long hours on hard wooden benches hadn't entered my mind. In short, I had a very low estimate of myself, and it was with a distinct feeling of discomfort that I greeted my guests for cocktails.

Catherine was a good girl. Throughout dinner she avoided talk of hospitals and medicine and listened to Josh and me rehearse our college pranks, letting us have our fun; but over coffee in the living-room she returned to the subject on her mind.

"Bertie," she began, "I do not believe you've ever in your life given serious thought to the human side of those dispensary patients, now have you?"

"I guess I haven't, Catherine. Not really. I've been too close to it and maybe too occupied treating their ills. Anyway, I'm not sure I'd have known what to do if——"

"You could at least have suggested making the places light and airy. If department stores can do that, certainly hospitals can."

"Costs money."

"What if it does? Hospitals can get all the money they want if they go at it right. And those awful benches!"

"They are bad, aren't they?"

"Relics of the Middle Ages. I suppose hospitals always have had benches in their smelly waiting-rooms and it never occurs to them not to. Why can't they put in rows of nicely-cushioned seats like those in theatres? Because they cost money, too, and they wear out? Don't make me laugh. You and your group never thought of it. It never occurred to you that the least you could do for sick and worried and unhappy people is to make them comfortable while they nervously wait to be seen by you. Not in dispensaries, that is. Not the down-and-outers. You jolly well do in your offices, though!"

There wasn't any use answering, because I didn't have a leg to stand on. Besides, I was becoming tremendously interested and wanted to know what ideas she might have.

"You know what I think?" she said. "Dispensaries, hospital waiting-rooms should be completely and entirely rebuilt and rearranged and it ought to be made compulsory. They should be much more spacious and pleasant looking. People shouldn't be made to sit in rows, and there should be comfortable chairs, even some easy-chairs, yes, even some couches. And lights, floor lights, or if not those, certainly good indirect soft lighting. Air conditioning goes without saying and—and small pleasant rest-rooms off the main one, where women can have privacy. Not the usual smelly toilets. I would provide nurseries and play-rooms for children, and skilled attendants, plenty of them, sympathetic ones."

"You amaze me."

"But I'm not through. Why shouldn't there be some music—not all the time, but occasionally throughout the day? Different kinds of music, perhaps, soft and soothing mostly. You could experiment. In fact, you could experiment in the whole business of dispensaries, and now that I think of it I wonder why it wasn't done a long time ago."

I was dumbfounded. I couldn't believe my ears. "Listen, darling. Where in the world did you get all these fanciful ideas?"

"But they're not fanciful!" she insisted, "or shouldn't be. And what's more, why shouldn't you have movies in dispensaries, not those requiring dark rooms, but things shown on special screens in the regular light, or possibly with the light dimmed—little amusing or instructive shorts, maybe a funny or a travel thing. Not continuously, but every once in a while. Wouldn't that take patients' minds off their troubles, if only momentarily?"

I admitted that it might.

"Wouldn't the children like it and could it possibly do harm to anyone, make their fever go up or increase their pain?"

I doubted it.

"You could also do a bit of instructing that way, too," Catherine proceeded relentlessly. "And in several different languages. Mothers could be told how to care for their babies, venereal diseases could be discussed, all sorts of subjects could be touched upon, and if there wasn't too much of it I have no doubt something would be accomplished."

"Golly!" I cried. "You've certainly given me a lot to think about."

"Finally, there's food," Catherine went on. "Did it ever occur to you doctors that the people out on the benches could do with a bit of food, a glass of milk, a sandwich? You told me yourself that they have to get in early for registration and that in any case they are early risers. Couldn't you have attendants pass among them from time to time offering milk or something equally innocuous, but sustaining? And wouldn't that make for better feeling all around, to say nothing of keeping children quiet? I wouldn't think the seriously ill would take anything much, and I certainly think that would be much better than having that little stand stuck away in a corner where people who know about it can go and buy a little something."

"In brief, as I understand her," Josh broke in, "Catherine would make dispensaries havens of refuge in a real sense;

she'd give them warmth and in so far as is humanly possible create an atmosphere of welcome and friendliness and comfort, so that the timid would lose their fears and the tired and worn out would have rest. Thus the actual medical phase would be less prominently displayed and people would come before the doctors in a better frame of mind and with greater courage and more hope. I think she's got something, Bertie, and nothing would give me greater pleasure than to see you incorporate some of her ideas in this great clinic. Ours will perhaps be too small to utilise them all, but I can assure you that you'll find most of them there when the place is finished."

"You wouldn't think it's all too Utopian?" I hated to say it.

"You want sick people to come to your hospitals and you want to doctor them, don't you?"

"Certainly."

"Well, woo them, make your place alluring, stop treating them like cattle, stop pushing them around and acting as if they're there on sufferance. I don't believe you doctors begin to appreciate the element of psychology in dispensary patients."

She had me and I knew it. "Our dispensary building isn't so old," I protested, "hardly twelve years, in fact. And we thought we did a good job, what with all the new wrinkles and things we put in, but—but—well, after listening to you, I'd say we completely lacked imagination and are still in the dark ages."

Catherine smiled at me. "Yes, you are, and what are you going to do about it?"

Do! I thought of the board members. I thought of the continual demands for money, always money, never enough to meet the needs of a great hospital, and I wondered. What would the board think of motion pictures and free lunches and overstuffed chairs?

Catherine could read my mind.

"Now that you have the idea I know you'll get your teeth into it. But let me give you a tip. This is a woman's job. Don't you have women on your board? Show them and you'll get somewhere."

I present to you women who read this book Catherine's ideas, which are so sound psychologically, so obvious and sensible that we doctors must have been blind as moles not to have thought of them long ago. Now that she has opened my eyes, I shall do what one man can do, for I know full well that she is right. If the women who are giving to hospitals generously of their time and their resources, in every town and city in America, would each sit for three hours in the waiting-room of their dispensary, it would be modernised, revolutionised, if you will, in no time at all. The musty odour of charity would disappear, and the sick would spend their long hours of waiting in an atmosphere that would give them comfort, ease their anxiety, and—after all, why not—give them a little pleasure.

15

NEEDED, A MILLION NURSES

DO YOU REALISE HOW WOEFULLY WE IN AMERICA ARE UNDER-nursed? To what extent depends upon a number of things: whether we live in city, town, or country, how much money we make, how much money we have, our various ills, hospitalisation—all sorts of things. But in round figures we have some 200,000 active doctors and some 300,000 active trained nurses—a ratio of 1 to 1½, in a population of 140,000,000 people.

Now, I should say that if 200,000 doctors are sufficient, 300,000 nurses are not. Even if you raise the latter figure by some 100,000 (a guess) to include all the so-called practical nurses and other unregistered, untrained personnel who help out with the sick for pay, it wouldn't be high enough. That would mean two nurses to each doctor, and one only has to listen to the present outcry about the nurse shortage to know that this is terribly, hopelessly inadequate.

More to the point would be accurate figures on what the doctor-nurse ratio *ought* to be; but little or no information is forthcoming on this subject and for the reason that it hasn't received sufficient attention. The same can be said of the nurse-patient ratio and the doctor-nurse-patient ratio, both extremely important considerations in the evaluation of present health measures and of those that will be taken in the near future. I am talking of sick people in the aggregate, that is, in their homes as well as in hospitals.

So we are compelled to postpone to a later date specula-
tion on a proper nurse-doctor ratio and go on to the
improper one that we know exists. The war catapulted
the problem into our laps, but in all probability it was
present long years before, only we didn't know it. We
didn't know it because all along we have been thinking of
sickness too much, almost exclusively, in fact, in terms of
doctors, medical schools, hospitals, plasma, X-ray, medicine,
penicillin, the sulfas. We still are, as is shown by the moves
and counter-moves of the government and of organised
medicine in the matter of medical care and by the activities of the Blue Cross and private agencies in hospitalisation. You have read little or nothing about the trained-
nurse problem and you have heard less.

Maybe this is proper and for the best, but again maybe
it isn't. I think it isn't. I think the great minds—even
those in medicine—have failed to appreciate the trained
nurse's growing importance in modern life and the
American scheme of things generally. Doctors appreciate
her, they put her on their cases and in their operating-
room, but they take her for granted as a sort of adjunct
that just grew and, while useful, demands no special attention. No proper recognition, other than lip service, has
been given the nurse's true place in modern medicine, and
if proof of that is needed it can be found in the lack of any
dynamic interest taken by the medical profession (as dis-
tinguished from the nursing profession) in developing and
providing for an adequate nursing corps.

The problem has been left almost exclusively to the
women, and the women have done a good job according
to their lights; but their lights have been too dim and
have lacked the penetration that the situation demands.
How could it possibly be otherwise? They haven't had the

first-hand knowledge required—knowledge and field experience comparable to that of doctors, who see the sick in every nook and corner of the land, especially the poor sick who never have a trained nurse and are lucky if they see an occasional visiting or health nurse. It's probable that these people comprise three-fourths of all the ill.

Let us look for a moment at present-day trends in nurse training. It is all geared for quality and not for quantity. As a result it isn't geared to meet the conditions prevailing among sick people: the poor as well as the rich, those who live in towns and villages as well as in cities, those in the hospitals, at home, the seriously ill, the slightly ill, men, women, and children. It is folly to have all nurses spend three years in training and to demand two years in some cases, or maybe four years of college work, for entrance to nursing schools. We can't get quantity that way and we've got to have quantity as well as quality if we're going to do the nursing job that has to be done. Only part of the nursing personnel need have the arduous three-year training—the teachers, the supervisors, the operating-room nurses, the nurses for the very sick.

I have no objection to higher education. On the contrary, I'm all for it. But what does the average trained nurse do that takes her such long years to learn? Why wouldn't it be much better for her and the sick if she spent more time on the wards and less in the class-room? I lecture to the student nurses of two hospitals myself and they listen attentively, but they are too young and immature and haven't the background to understand surgery of the stomach and intestines. Furthermore, I don't see what that has to do with taking temperatures, making beds, counting pulses, giving treatments, keeping records—or even making observations. If you say it gives them more interest and makes them more intelligent, I might agree, but they could get the same interest and the same intelligence while walking the wards and handling patients. Perhaps I might add that in the opinion of most doctors, nurses in training remember much of the material they are taught in the class-room only long enough to stand their State Boards and then they forget it. Nurse after nurse has admitted as much to me.

I put this to you straight because the nation urgently needs thousands of women who can do practical nursing. A beginning has to be made at turning them out, and it is a 'must' that admits of no delay. You can't have a hospital without trained nurses, any more than you can have one without doctors—not in these modern days; even if the scarcity of nurses is acute now, think what it will be when we begin to put up all the new hospitals needed for war veterans and people of the hinterlands. It's real, the plans for those hospitals are in existence, and nursing personnel to man them has to be provided in advance, not afterwards. Nurses can't be trained overnight. Also their sphere of activities goes far beyond hospital walls. By the thousands they are engaged in people's homes and in public health and industry, with the demand for their services daily broadening. Many a young girl would gladly take up nursing as a profession but is deterred at the thought of spending three years in training with no pay or at best nominal pay.

Only the doctors can set this matter of the nurses straight. Only the doctors by their insistence and by the logic of their reasoning can bring home the fact that however wonderful it is to have quality in nurses, there must also be quantity. You can't have an army composed entirely of officers, and that is what we have now in the nurses.

They are all West Point and Annapolis graduates, as it were, and no finer body of women exists anywhere in the world; but to fulfill their purpose they must have an enlisted personnel. This personnel will need only the training given enlisted personnel in other walks of life, sufficient, that is, to equip them for the field work, the heavy duty, the long hours, and the stiff fighting that are the lot of private soldiers. Advancement from the ranks to officer group should not only be offered to them but adequate provision for it should be made.

I do not think that 300,000 officer-nurses will be too many for tomorrow's nurse army, and so I do not feel that the existing training schools need be scrapped or changed. It may even be that certain of these schools will have to provide for advanced training of special groups, and without doubt more attention will have to be paid to post-graduate study. For the most part, however, new and different schools will have to be inaugurated, schools in which high-school graduates, or girls having the equivalent education, will be trained as enlisted personnel to fight illness and disease exactly as our young boys of these late years were turned into enlisted personnel of the armed forces to fight the enemies of our country. There are only 1,295 schools for nursing now in existence in America, and the average enrolment is but 98 students. There are, however, some 6,000 hospitals, and in a few short years there will be 500 or perhaps 1,000 more. No difficulty whatever should be encountered in starting new schools, because many hospitals that may not be in a position to train nurses of the higher category may well be able to train those in the lower grade. One can visualise enrolments of 10 to 25 student nurses for one year's practical training in hundreds of hospitals that now have no nurses' training school, with great advantage to hospitals, patients, and students alike.

I cannot feel that it is an insult to the nursing profession to suggest that it train young women to do different types of nursing—and grade them and permit registration accordingly—or that it would amount to a lowering of standards if they did. Indeed, I think there is entirely too much talk about standards and too little about the pressing need of the sick, which is for nursing of a practical nature—one year's training. And by practical nature I mean taking temperatures, counting pulses, bathing, feeding, servicing, giving medicines as ordered, and simple treatments—all the dozens of things a woman of tact and common sense can do for one who is ill. Surely such a woman could tell the doctor if the patient looks better or worse or is coughing more or maybe is restless, and I do not think it would be asking too much of her to keep some sort of a chart.

I do not include in so-called practical nursing the taking of blood pressures, the giving of blood transfusions and other intravenous treatments, any more than I would include passing a stomach tube or making blood counts. These are things the doctor or specially trained technician should do. If the truth be known, that is where the great mistake is being made in the nursing of the day. Too much emphasis has been laid on the special training and too little on the practical. The highly trained nurse has gradually arrogated to herself—aided to no small degree by busy doctors—duties that never were intended to be those of nurses. Thus it has come about that too many nurses have a feeling of superiority and refuse to do or object to the menial part of their work. They refuse to do nursing outside of hospitals. They limit themselves to certain types of cases. They refuse night work and work over the week-end. Need I go further? Can't you see that the day of reckoning is at hand and that if nursing is to fulfil its true mission it must return to its original concepts?

I admit freely that there are difficulties and that many of them have to do with the time we are living in. One might as well face facts. Girls as well as boys want their evenings and week-ends free, and when it comes to work they want to be paid for the work they do, and they want short hours, and employment of a kind that has few, if any, unpleasant features. Little wonder they have refused utterly to join a profession that to date has shown little or no understanding of their viewpoint and scant willingness to meet the problem.

The medical profession as well as the nursing profession is responsible, and together they will have to face the problem. They've got to do even more. They will have actually to woo young women to take up nursing. To compensate for the unpleasant phases of the work and the danger involved they will have to discover means to make it attractive, and money is the starting-point. The girl in training, the graduate nurse should be guaranteed adequate remuneration, remuneration at least equal to and probably greater than what she would make in other fields. This thing of giving nurses in training a pittance in addition to their living is ridiculous. They do a full day's work and more and should be paid accordingly. Their exploitations should cease. Nor is that all. The restraints put upon them after working hours should be reviewed and drastically changed—in their favour. The nation has to have nurses. Short of drafting young women for training in nursing, similar to drafting boys for military training, the only possible way to get them in is to meet their terms. The matter is no different from meeting the terms of people in other walks of life. Heads of the nursing profession only think it is. They are so far out of touch as to keep mouthing a lot of old stuff about high duty, self-sacrifice, the "call", and such!

This problem is all the more poignant because the whole picture of medical care and attention is undergoing changes brought about as much by newer social concepts as by scientific medical advance. The nursing impasse is but the reflection of it. The newer medical advances require more knowledge, more involved tests, special apparatus, and, equally important, more attention. Doctors tend, therefore, to be more and more insistent that their patients come into the hospital. There are none too many doctors at best, and they haven't time to go from house to house as they once did. Moreover, the Blue Cross and private insurance agencies have put hospitalisation within the reach of millions who formerly couldn't afford it, and so hospital rooms and hospital wards the nation over are constantly filled, with more patients clamouring to get in. Even the storks fuss and fume nowadays at the very idea of carrying babies to the home!

This is all fine for the doctors and it is the proper way to do modern medicine. No one denies this, and the results obtained, quite aside from the patient's comfort, are much better than when doctoring was done chiefly in the home. But the change came too fast and we weren't ready for it either in hospitals or in nursing, especially in the latter. I don't think this point has been made hitherto. Certainly it has never been stressed or made really clear, yet it is the crux of the whole matter. By the very fact that pressure on the doctors has been relieved, that on the nurses has increased. And I'm not talking about private nurses for private patients, individual nursing. I'm talking of nurses in general, chiefly hall or floor nurses so called—the ones who do general duty and run up and down wards and halls a hundred times and more a day, doing all things, big and little, that go to make the sick more comfortable and their recovery more certain.

Every time you admit a patient into a hospital, you need more nursing, whether the patient is free or pay, in a room or a ward, man, woman, or child. And it isn't merely a question of medicines and operations. It's a question of ordinary living. Patients have to eat and they have to have a bed to sleep in. They have to bathe or be bathed and either serve themselves or be served. The patients who are very sick just make the going tougher—for the personnel, that is. Prior to the up-surge of hospital insurance, it was rare for hospitals to be filled to the brim, and then it was only for comparatively short periods, chiefly during epidemics or at the height of the pneumonia season. And that wasn't all. There were recognised slack seasonal periods when whole floors or wards and private rooms were closed. Painting and cleaning went on and repair work, and doctors and nurses and personnel generally were given time off.

Thus it happened that training schools for nurses were almost static so far as the number of girls enrolled was concerned. Most of the larger hospitals train their own nurses and have been training only such numbers as they need, and their needs have not been computed on the basis of constant peak loads. True it was that when they had their peak loads, whether seasonal or through unexpected circumstances, the nursing personnel had hard sledding, but it was always possible to hire extra graduate nurses to come in and do general-duty work because extra nurses were available. Some hospitals even took nurses away from private patients who weren't especially ill, so one way or another the emergency was met.

It is a fact, however, that the true import of coming events, as evidenced by the great appeal the Blue Cross hospitalisation idea is making to the people, was not appreciated even when hospitals began to lose their slack periods and to become chronically filled to capacity. So far as my observations go, few hospitals enlarged their nursing-school enrolments appreciably, before the war. In other words, the aggregate of trained nurses being turned out each year did not increase as much as it should have or would have if hospital authorities had been alert to what was going on. I should say that communities weren't either, because if they had been they'd have put up many more hospitals. The actual number of students nurses in America in 1935 was 67,533. Six years later in 1941 it was only 87,588, and in view of the growing need—let alone the prospect of war—that was a very small increase. Once the war began we saw the enrolment of United States Cadet Nurses, numbering 85,042 in 1944 and 110,068 in 1945. Now that has ceased.

It wasn't a case of the nation having more sick people than usual. It was only that more of them had been sold on the idea of going to the hospital when ill, and the various new plans for hospitalisation insurance had put them in a position to do so. Moreover, they had more money once the war came and wages sky-rocketed. A new and different idea had seized upon the public imagination, and whereas sick people in volume had previously looked askance at going to hospitals, there now was a complete about-face and they were hell-bent for it. Never in my long medical life have I witnessed such a metamorphosis— or a happier one for the long term; never have I known the medical profession, the nursing profession, hospital and civic authorities caught more off guard, or slower to see and evaluate the consequences and meaning of the movement.

I dare say the ever-increasing hospital load would sooner or later of itself have given rise to the inevitable problem of the nurses, but the war undoubtedly hastened it and blew the flames of discontent as high as the sky, spreading the sparks far and wide. People were disturbed, but took it in good part through patriotism—as they took other things that might have been avoided—but it was bad and there's no use denying it. Maybe it's just another one of the penalties we pay for being a democracy. That's the charitable view, and one cannot blame or criticise any one group when all groups were equally oblivious to modern trends and therefore equally responsible.

More to the point is how we are going to work our way out. It is my opinion that nothing worth while will be accomplished without giving nursing full equality with doctoring and hospitalisation. In other words, medical care and attention for the sick henceforth must be a tripartite arrangement, instead of the dual affair that it has been. It will serve no good purpose to work out doctor projects—co-operative, group, prepayment, and so on—to meet all incomes, or to put up hospitals here, there, everywhere, unless provisions are made for nursing on a similar basis. By no stretch of the imagination will the sick of the lower-income brackets ever get nursing unless this is done, and failure to do so will be but an admission that we are callous to their needs and requirements.

Indeed I foresee increasing pressure to compel the Blue Cross as well as other agencies to include some private nursing in their hospitalisation policies—perhaps eight hours of nursing per any one week, twenty-four hours' maximum for the total three weeks, to be taken all together or in periods of two or four hours per day or night as desired or as ordered by the doctor. Only the very ill require nurses in constant attendance, and the present-day custom of having private nurses sitting around holding their patients' hands or doing little things that don't need doing—even annoying their patients with their attentions —is not only unrealistic but shockingly wasteful.

We need badly to revamp our ideas of nursing. Plainly the vast majority of the sick in or out of hospitals need but a few hours of private nursing per day—in the morning, perhaps, or at bed-time. If the idea of twenty-four hours' maximum of private nursing over a three-week period seems at first glance hardly worth while, merely a sop thrown out to poor people, the broken-period idea might well place the proposal in a different light. The heat is already on to include doctors fees in hospitalisation, and if that can be done, as I have no doubt it can, there is no good reason why the additional step of nursing cannot be included. Later, prepayment or insurance medicine will include nursing for the sick who remain at home. Here I think that the need would be met by the visiting type of nurse—an hour or so a day or twice a day for those more ill.

However, this whole thing will be little more than an empty gesture unless the nursing body is increased and put on a proper basis. To that end I see in my mind's eye half a million practical nurses of one year's training, all registered and amenable to the rules and regulations of the nursing profession, all officered and guided by that more highly trained group. This would give a nurse-doctor ratio of 4 to 1—800,000 nurses—which would do for a starter. When we discover by investigation what the ratio ought to be, appropriate measures can be taken to bring it into better line. Knowing what I do about outlying districts and about districts not so outlying, having studied and given much thought to the plight of the under-privileged sick in general and foreseeing the dynamic quality of tomorrow's medicine with special emphasis to be laid on prevention of illness, it would be my suggestion that the medical and nursing professions stop talking so much about the difficulties of the nurse problem and solve them. Either that or admit their inability and let someone else do it for them. It can be done.

16

THE PROBLEMS OF THE
YOUNG SURGEON

IT HADN'T BEEN AN EXCEPTIONALLY DIFFICULT OPERATION— just troublesome and a bit tedious, as some goitres can be. The woman had come in rather toxic, but she was fairly young, she had yielded nicely to pre-operative preparation, and her general condition was good. We had taken our time with the operation, for there hadn't been need for hurry. There wasn't any now, and as the wound closure proceeded, young Crowley, the first assistant and resident surgeon who was working with me, occupied my mind. His term of service would be over in a couple of months and he would be going out into practice.

"What do you plan to do when you leave, Phil?" I asked.

"Starve mostly, I guess," said the boy, and the whole team laughed.

"Oh, it's not that bad. Pick up that little vessel in the muscle there and tie it. That's good. What I meant was have you decided where to locate?" He hadn't been in to talk things over as most of his predecessors had done, and I'd noticed he was becoming less communicative.

"No, sir. That is, not exactly."

"Well, plenty of time. Skin suture, please."

There was silence.

"You have to take extra care in closing these neck wounds," I remarked. "People don't like unsightly scars; especially if they show."

It was the end of the day and a good day as things went,

with all five operations going off on schedule and no unusual happenings. I decided to make another attempt to pierce my young friend's armour. He was a good fellow, honest and hard working, but sometimes a little uncertain of himself. Fortunately, he was not married; at least I thought that was fortunate, because I knew he had scant resources and had been compelled to work part of his way through college. As the nurse was helping me out of my operating-room regalia it occured to me that now was as good a time as any to have a little chat, and so before going to the dressing-room I casually drifted over to where Phil was giving post-operative directions to the nurse in charge and invited him in to see me.

"Change into something dry and come in for a cigarette, Phil," I said. "And after that we'll go make rounds a bit."

He smiled and said thanks he'd be glad to.

"Phil," I said, when he had lighted up, "what's on your mind?"

"Well, doctor, it's a tough business this deciding where to go and all. You know that better than I do."

"Yes, I guess so. But we all have to go through it."

"I know, and I'd rather go back to Texas where I came from, only——"

"Only what?" I prompted. "A girl?"

"Yes, sir."

Many ambitious young surgeons, if left to their own devices, would start practice in the wide open spaces where the wait isn't so long because they are needed there and opportunity is on their very doorsteps. And it isn't that the girl objects so much as that they themselves don't want to put their wives, and the children that will come, through the hardships of a kind of living—and lonesomeness—they are not used to and might not like; that, together with the lack of good hospitals and libraries and medical schools, the isolation from the big medical centres and the lack of high-grade medicine in general to which they've been conditioned through their years of study and general preparation.

Crowley came in several times after that to see me, but in spite of our talks he finally decided to remain in the big city and sweat it out. He had only grinned when I said there's always room at the top. My own chief had told me that years before when the time came for my decision, and I was just passing it along. I didn't tell him what my own observation had been—that there was far more room at the bottom—because his mind had been made up and there was no use discouraging him.

"Think you could find a place for me in your out-patient department?" he asked.

"Gladly. After you get settled go see Dr. Goodrich and he'll put you to work. Of course you realise the job pays nothing."

"I know, but it's a chance to keep busy."

He was silent and I knew what was coming.

"You—that is, doctor, you wouldn't have a paying job or know of one, would you?"

"No. I'm sorry."

"That's the trouble. I don't mind doing most anything for nothing, but a fellow's got to live."

"He sure does. Have you tried to get an insurance job or one with an industrial concern? I'd be glad to give you a note."

"Thanks a lot. I'll ask you for one if the chance comes. And that reminds me to ask if I can send in for operation a private case or so." He grinned and added: "If I get one."

"Yes, indeed."

And we left it at that, except that later on I advanced him three hundred dollars to buy office equipment, and noted that shortly after his marriage he opened up in the poorer district of the city with a small, unpretentious office in the home of his in-laws. The girl was lovely and taught school.

"Did you know Phil Crowley sent an appendectomy in last night, sir?" The new resident, Crowley's successor, was speaking. We were just finishing an appendectomy ourselves—his first with me on the other side of the table— and he had handled himself well.

"No, I hadn't heard. Go all right?"

"It did and it was a honey."

"Ruptured?"

"Not quite, and old Phil did a swell job."

"Bully!"

There was silence as the youngster put in the last few stitches.

"Phil's going to do well. Straight shooter, too."

"Aren't they all?" I asked innocently.

The boy looked up. "Now, doctor," he said, and I could see he was grinning.

But Phil didn't do well, and after some seven or eight months he came and told me he thought after all he would go back to Texas.

"How about the wife, Phil? Is she agreeable now?"

"She's the one who's urging it."

I was just about to start my third operation, a gall-bladder affair, and, as had been his custom after finishing his regular dispensary work, the young surgeon had come to the operating-room to look on.

"A fellow gets rusty doing no operating, doctor," he had said to me one day, "and if it's all the same to you, I think I'll spend my spare time watching you and the other staff men work."

"That's bully, son, and I'd have suggested it myself, but sometimes it's best to let the beginner work out his own salvation."

He smiled and I said nothing more at the moment, but his attitude pleased me and I made every effort to make his attendance worth while. At the same time, it was a little disturbing to find him spending so much time there, and as the weeks turned into months the residents rarely mentioned his doing a case of his own. Upon two occasions when the opportunity offered I had had the front office refer small cases to him, but you can't do too much of that because unassigned cases that carry a fee are supposed to go to the older men who have given years of service to the hospital. None of them receives pay, and this is the only legitimate way the hospital has of favouring them.

So when Crowley finally decided to pull up stakes it didn't surprise me.

"Stick around for this thing," I said, "and then let's have a cigarette. Maybe I can give you a bit of a steer."

"O.K.," he replied, and for the next hour or so, though the others among the visitors did considerable talking—it wasn't a difficult case—Crowley kept mum. He was never very talkative, but every once in a while, usually towards the end when the others were beginning to leave, he would put in a question or two or make some reference to what had gone before that showed his interest and general alertness.

"How'd you come to make up your mind to make a fresh start, Phil?" I started in immediately after my shower.

"Oh, I don't know, sir. Got to eat, I guess."

"Doesn't Old Man McGrain feed you?" I laughed.

"That's the trouble. He does, and I can't pay my share."

"Takes time for a surgeon to get going."

"I'll say, but——"

"But what?"

"We-e-ll, maybe I'm a gripe."

I decided not to press him. If he wanted to talk he'd have to do it himself. Otherwise . . .

"Listen, doctor," he finally blurted out, "this thing of a fellow spending ten years or more learning how to operate on the goitres and stomachs and pelvic stuff and—and at his own expense, and then at the end, when he's flat broke, being thrown out in the world and told to go make a living is all wrong."

"You surprise me. I'd have sworn it was fee-splitting."

"Oh, that!" he said with disgust. "What I meant was that just when fellows like me get to the point where we could do good surgery, you won't give us any to do in your hospitals, and we can't get it on the outside. People don't like young surgeons, or at least they don't trust them, and physicians don't dare give anything to them except maybe boils and little things. It makes me sick!"

He was working himself up to a pitch, and I let him proceed.

"How do you expect me to keep on being a good surgeon if I never get a chance to use the knife? How can I go anywhere but backward? And how long is this period of waiting my turn and cooling my heels going to last, for God's sake?"

"It *is* a ridiculous system, isn't it?"

"Ridiculous! Idiotic describes it better. Old guys who have plenty of operating to do in their private practices hold on like grim death to their services and won't let a younger man have a bit of work. I would be willing to wait my turn for private stuff, and so would many others in my predicament, if it were only possible to keep my hand in; but no, you won't allow that. So what happens? I forget how to do the gall-bladders and the goitres and the sotmachs I worked so hard to get proficient in, and by the time they begin to come my way years hence, when I'm grey and maybe bald, I won't be able to do them or, at best, will do them badly."

"Aren't you exaggerating?"

"No, sir, I'm not, and you know it."

I had no good answer and my heart was heavy. Everything the boy said was true. The House of Medicine had built him up into an operating surgeon—at his own expense, not at its expense or society's—and just when he was able to use his wings, just when, by his youth and exuberance, he might be expected to want to try them out, that same house said: "No, my son, it is written in the book that you are not to be permitted to do that, but must go out and grub for the little things and half starve and eat your heart out—for long years."

Crowley was speaking again, and I noticed he had leaned forward and held his face in his hands.

"Forgive me, doctor," he said in a half-muffled voice, "I didn't mean to take it out of you and, of course, it isn't your fault. But you asked for it and I let you have it. I think if I get out where there aren't so many surgeons maybe there'll be work for me. Myrtle thinks so, too, and we mean to give it a try."

I could have wept—it was so tragic, and I was so utterly

helpless. That boy, that sensitive, educated, highly trained product of our present-day medical system—which we take such pride in—was not the exception. He was the rule. All young surgeons are compelled to tread the same road. Nobody thinks of them and nobody holds out a helping hand. Older entrenched surgeons see in them competitors, and fear them. Hospital authorities cannot give them ward work because older, more experienced men hog it all. The most they can do is to let them work in the out-patient departments, but there are no funds with which to pay them even a pittance. The hospitals do give them the privilege of sending in patients who have the money to pay for private accommodations, but that is a doubtful privilege at best, because patients have been told to beware of young wielders of the knife and stick to the old ones who really know how.

Surgery is different from medicine in that only one man can do a given operation, while a dozen can examine and prescribe for a patient medically ill. People will give the young physician a trial, feeling that they don't have to take his medicines if they don't care to, and in any case if he makes a mistake they can always call in old Dr. Smith who only lives a few blocks away, and can surely correct it before harm is done. Nobody can correct a slip of the knife.

What we need is a new and better system; it is still a long way off, but it is coming. With the war and a general appreciation of the fact that people living in sparsely settled areas have as much right to good medical care and attention as have those living in and around metropolitan centres, the outlook has changed materially. It won't be long now before you will see first-aid stations and hospitals, big and little, dotted everywhere throughout the land. The government will put up some, states and communities will put up others (with or without government aid), and private individuals will finance still others.

They and their laboratories will have to be equipped and staffed with doctors, nurses, technicians, and order-lies. Around certain of these places, the more strategically located, medical centres with research facilities will be established, and it is not beyond the possibilities that the occasional one will have a medical school attached. These developments are logical and of the utmost importance. The other prime necessity is the paying of good salaries to the doctors who will be required to man these places. That is the only way you'll get good doctors to go out to them, especially the highly trained youngsters of today, who, however poor and pushed around and forgotten, still are ambitious and prefer to starve in the metropolitan centres than to go out and live in the provinces.

I believe in facing facts and being realistic, and while others put forward high-sounding educational and socio-logical plans for the distribution of young doctors to out-lying districts, I adhere to the thesis that money talks. You can put up all the beautiful hospitals and medical centres and laboratories you want out in the far-flung regions and you can build parks and swimming-pools and promise band concerts and operas and you still won't get the boys you really want unless you offer them good pay. And even with money many of them won't be satisfied and won't stay. It's a big problem and will take time and thought to solve.

I do think, though, that the young surgeon will be well advised to jump at these jobs. He'll get work there immediately and be busy, and that will keep him from worrying. He'll get a living wage from the start, sufficient to marry and support a wife and children. He'll probably get a house to live in and low rent; and if the various projects are managed well, physicians of quality and other medical men, including scientists, will take similar jobs, and there will develop a social and professional life of extreme importance. Whether the clinical men will remain full time on salary or be permitted or encouraged to build up private practices in the areas round about and become part-time men is something that time and experience alone will tell. I hope surgeons will not, and for reasons that I have already given. I do think, however, that a system of promotion will have to be developed whereby good work, aptitude, and scientific production will receive adequate recognition. No man ought to be condemned to live where he doesn't want to, and it is hardly to be expected that he will accept employment away from the large centres unless promise of advancement is held out to him. Money talks, but not that loud to men of worth, and they are the ones you must have if you are to succeed. They must have incentive, and only the chance for advancement to a more important post will answer that need.

So while I pity the young surgeon as the system exists today, I see a rainbow on his horizon, and it isn't by any means as far away as it used to be.

17

THEY, TOO, MUST LIVE

SOME TIME BACK I WAS BROUGHT UP SHARP BY FEE-SPLITTING among doctors, and in a way that was anything but pleasant. In case you are somewhat hazy about this secretive practice, let me quote a simple definition from a former book of mine. "Fee-splitting is the division *without the patient's knowledge*, of the money a surgeon collects for a given operation with the physician who refers him the case." Some physicians demand a bigger cut than others, some surgeons give a bigger cut. The custom does not necessarily increase the fee to the patient, but among the dangers lies the fact that a few physicians, only a few, I should say, hawk their work around to the highest bidder. In spite of the naïve and high-sounding pledge signed by the members of the American College of Surgeons, the general impression is that the custom is widespread throughout the country and is growing.

The incident that brought fee-splitting rudely home to me was a conversation with a friend, Gus Henkel, a physician of quality and fine character with whom I chanced to be journeying to a medical meeting. He remarked, rather innocently I thought, that he'd seen one of my men just a few days back and had been handed thirty dollars by him.

"That's nice. I'm glad my men pay their debts. Who was it?"

"Bob Andrews, and he wasn't returning borrowed money. He was giving me my cut."

"Your what?"

"My cut out of the fee he collected from a mutual patient. She had to have her uterus scraped."

He was half laughing and I could see that he was teasing, but it wasn't funny.

"What's the story behind the story?" I growled. "I guess there is one."

"Yes, there is," he replied, and his face became serious. "Andrews was one of your officers, wasn't he?"

"Yes, and a good man."

"Nice fellow, too, but poor like most of them and married when he shouldn't be. Has a kid. He settled out my way and, as usual with young surgeons, sat in his office waiting for cases that didn't come and studying and biting his nails. I sent him one or two little things, and that's how I know. He took to dropping in to see me and—well, money got tighter and tighter and I loaned him a hundred dollars and then another. He couldn't pay it back, and I didn't press him, but several times he remarked that it was a helluva thing for a man of his training to sit tight and do nothing while other men of the same age and far less training and little ability had all they could do. I knew what he meant and indirectly tried to bolster his fading morale, but once they start griping in earnest they rarely hold out. He might have, at that, if it hadn't been for the wife and kid, because he has guts. But no man is going to stand by and watch his family suffer when all he has to do is reach out and take what is offered."

"I guess not."

"That was just about eight months ago, and for a time I lost sight of him because I was busy. Just about two weeks ago, though, I had occasion to see a woman who had done an abortion on herself, and casting about in a hurry for someone to take care of her, I thought of Andrews and called him. The thirty dollars was half the fee he collected from a very grateful patient, and as he laid it on my desk his face turned red and his voice broke as he said: 'Don't think too hard of me, doctor.' "

"My God!"

Gus was thoughtfully silent.

"What'd you do and what'd you say to him, Gus?"

"I told him he should keep the money, that I didn't want it and couldn't accept it. The case I'd given him was his without any strings attached."

"Did he take it?"

"No, he didn't. He refused absolutely, so I'm going to give it to the Red Cross. But that wasn't so important as what he had to say."

"What was that?"

"He told me: 'Doctor, I wrestled with this thing of fee-splitting until I couldn't sleep any more. They are all doing it around here, physicians as well as surgeons—all except the older and best-established ones—and the fellow that refuses to divide gets no work. I did my level best and even argued and pleaded with physicians I knew, but they just laughed and said I was a fool. So after a year of half starvation and seeing my wife and kid going around bedraggled and unhappy, I decided that medical ethics were all wrong when it came to taking a man's living away from him, and I was going to have none of it. After all, surgeons and their families have to live, too—young as well as old.' "

"Did you remonstrate?"

"How could I? I think he's right."

"You what?" I stared at Gus as though he had lost his mind.

"That's right, I don't split fees myself, and I probably never will because I don't need to in the first place, and I guess I'm too thin-skinned in the second place. But that doesn't mean I haven't noticed what's going on around me and tried in my own way to dope it out."

"I don't believe I've faced up to it," I confessed. "Been too busy."

"That's the trouble with you older men," protested Gus. "You're too damn busy; only I know you're not. That's just the excuse you use to keep from facing up to things that are embarrassing and maybe a bit hot to handle. You mean to sit there and tell me you don't know all these young kids and lots of the older ones aren't buying and selling patients for all hell-fire, and the guy that won't join in might as well pack up his grips, sell his office equipment, and move on?"

"Of course I know it, or something of it."

"Well, why'n the hell haven't you said so and done something about it?"

"But what could I have done even if I had faced up to it? Ethics are ethics, and I don't make them or unmake them. Organised medicine says——"

"Oh, for God's sake, don't talk organised medicine to me, and if you had looked this thing square in the eye, you'd long since have gone to your brethren of the big-shot clique and begged them at least to take a sane, common-sense view of an urgent and practical problem."

We were sitting in the lounge car and had the whole evening before us. Henkel practised chiefly among the middle-income people and had a large and devoted following. I'd known him for years and respected him for his medical perspicacity and judgment. We didn't see each other often, and when we did it was usually medicine and

surgery that we discussed. This was the first time anything
connected with medical procedure had come up, and it was
clear that my friend had a great deal on his mind.

"It's this way, Bertie," he said. "Whenever money is involved there's trouble. That's human nature; whether it's
in business or in law or in medicine, men struggle for it.
The medical profession refuses to admit that fact and still
wants to play-act, as if doctors were different from other
people in money matters. The practising doctors of today—
that is, the fellows I'm talking about and they're probably
the majority—take the position that it is nobody's business
but their own how they divide the money collected from a
given patient in a given illness—and I can't see that it is,
either. The pledge you surgeons are made to sign to the
effect that you will not split fees is as silly and unrealistic
as our late lamented prohibition laws that only fostered
bootlegging."

"But you yourself say the boys buy and sell patients," I
protested, "and I take it you don't think so well of that."

"Of course they do. Some physicians sell to the highest
bidder and are not so careful about his having ability, but
they are mostly the riff-raff of the profession, the money-
grabbers pure and simple, the—the actual, downright bootleggers."

"I don't get it."

"Now, listen, Bertie," Gus said, in a long-suffering tone
of voice, "and try to think. The minute prohibition went
off the nation's books and the liquor business ceased to be a
racket the bootleggers were put completely out of business.
That is, for the most part. Wouldn't it be exactly the same
if the medical profession once and for all officially wiped
all pledges, laws, and every possible stigma attached to
dividing fees off the books?"

"Maybe, but I couldn't be sure."

"At least we could make a try. We could experiment and certainly we couldn't possibly be any worse off than we are now. Could we? Be honest."

I had to acknowledge that we couldn't be.

"Don't you think that a good many physicians who now give their surgery to poor or mediocre surgeons, because they are the only ones who will divide, would be inclined to give more to better surgeons if there were the same money in it for them—even, maybe, if there were somewhat less? They might actually give more of their surgery to them simply for the association and in order to shine in their reflected glory, for they, too, are human and like a little of the limelight."

I sat there silent.

"And every little bit they'd take away from the mediocre boys," Henkel went on, "and give you fellows would be that much gained, wouldn't it?"

"But aren't you forgetting the moral values, Gus?" I asked.

"How so?"

"The man that's low-down enough to give his work to a surgeon he knows is incapable, the man who is so callous to his patient's suffering and well-being, even his death, the fellow who has people operated on when they don't need it and just for the fee, would hardly change even if the laws and pledges were abrogated."

"We'd have to see," said Gus. "And that's what I had in mind when I said the profession would have to experiment. How else can we know what's in those fellows' minds or whether they are or are not wholly or fundamentally bad? And why should the profession not experiment in social as well as scientific matters, for God's sake?"

"It should, of course."

"I take you back to prohibition once more," insisted my friend, "and call to mind that people just naturally preferred the known, guaranteed values to the bootleg. That's human nature, Bertie, and I'm optimist enough to believe these low-down guys, as you call them—and some of them are that certainly—would sooner or later change over, too, if only for their own self-protection."

"Maybe. But," I argued, "there is still one more element you haven't taken into account. How about the big shots, the leaders of surgery? Do you think they'd divide their take with that third-rate doctor who has a miserable practice down in the slums and only produces a patient with a little money once in a blue moon?"

"Maybe you've got something there," admitted Gus, ruefully.

"They'd throw him out of their clinics if he so much as hinted at a cut or a kick-back even if medical ethics permitted it."

"You think so?"

"Sure as hell. They're a law unto themselves and demand and receive homage from all."

"You don't think they'd bow even to Mr. Average Doctor, who practises in nice neighbourhoods and has a good clientele?"

"No! Not those fellows. They don't need to."

"But more than all doctors they're certainly after the money," said Henkel.

"Yes, but——"

"And they've got secretaries, haven't they? Why couldn't the secretaries take the little guy in tow and make a dicker with him?"

"Maybe they could, at that," I admitted.

"What else are secretaries for?" Henkel was driving his point home. He went on to insist that we need a lot of experimenting—and not alone in fee-splitting; but in other social problems that cry out for it, too, and the sooner our organised medicine gets down to it the sooner we'll get some sense into this medical business.

He certainly sounded reasonable, but at the moment my mind had reverted to Andrews. I was more than a little upset about him and asked Gus what he really thought would happen.

"Oh, the usual thing," Gus answered. "Andrews will feel sheepish and probably keep out of your way for a while. His conscience will be hurting, but not for long. Fee-splitters always rationalise themselves into believing it's the right thing. With increasing prosperity will come confidence and the courage to brazen it out."

"What would you say I ought to do?"

"Nothing, and for heaven's sake don't think of refusing him hospital privileges. That would only drive him to other and poorer hospitals and less desirable associates. Besides which, there are plenty of other fee-splitters in your hospital group, only you don't know about them."

"You certainly have a practical mind, Henkel," I said finally.

"That's the only kind to have about things of a practical nature. Besides, the boys have a way of confiding in me." And with that a thoughtful look crept into his eyes, a look that bespoke the sympathy I knew he had not only for them, but for all mankind. "That's one reason I think I may have something in this little matter of fee-splitting," he added.

And I believe he does.

18

EMANCIPATION

I NEVER LIKED PRIVATE PRACTICE AND NO DOUBT THAT accounts for my not being a great success at it. You have to have a special flair and a spark if you're going to be good with people who pay for private medical service, and I had neither. With babies and youngsters I got along famously; when others couldn't do anything with them, I could; when others got mad and couldn't make them out, I could, and I rarely if ever lost my temper. But that wasn't enough! It isn't the youngsters who call you in or pay you. Since people said my bedside manner lacked warmth and was too professional, they thought me cold or high-hat or both.

As if that wasn't bad enough for my practice, I didn't get along with physicians any too well. I made the mistake of telling them what I thought and trying to do my own thinking—two of the worst mistakes a budding young surgeon can make. You've got to pick your man to do that, and fate made me a bad picker. The boys said I didn't understand them and was ornery to boot. If I didn't agree with their diagnosis and treatment I didn't have to blurt it right out before patient and family and maybe the kibitzers, too.

"There's an art to the practice of medicine, Bernheim," said Fred Baker to me one day, "and you haven't got it." He was disgusted. "Here I ask you in to see a simple appendix in a young unmarried girl, daughter of nice people, and what do you do but create suspicion in their minds that she didn't have an appendix at all, but something else—maybe something of a questionable nature."

"How do you make that out?" I asked.

"By the way you framed your questions, and your insistence upon a pelvic examination."

"But you wanted to know what the girl was suffering from, didn't you?"

"Of course, but there are ways and ways."

"Evidently, but why did you let her mother and all the others stand around while we questioned her?"

"Oh, God, forgive this man!" said Fred. "He's a good young doctor, but knows not the ways of people! Don't you know you can't drive the family out of the room in private practice, especially among the middle classes, and that to attempt it means loss of the family?"

"No."

"Well, you know it now, and what's more this isn't the first time you've been dumb or acted dumb and I'm sick of it. I like you and think you're good, but life's too short to bother with people who won't learn."

Fred was somewhat older than I and he had a good, big practice, but when it came to border-line surgical problems, even some that weren't so border-line, he could get himself into difficulties. I often wondered how it was that his patients stuck to him and swore by him the way they did. But he was a nice fellow; nothing was too much for him to do: he'd get out of bed and scramble down-town of a night to see his patients and do all the menial, dirty work other fellows wouldn't think of doing. That was probably what made him so beloved.

I liked Fred a lot and took to heart what he had said to me, but it didn't help much. The only cases he ever gave

me after that were big, difficult ones that nobody else
wanted, and those after the patients had already been sent
into the hospital. He never again had me come to the
patient's house.

But Baker wasn't the only doctor who took me to task.
About ten months later I got a good going over from
George Lynhurst. I somehow couldn't seem to learn and
this time it was about 2 a.m. of one of the hottest nights
of summer.

"Listen, Bernheim," Lynhurst said the moment we came
out of the oven-like house of the Sam Obermeyers, "when
I call you in for an acute appendix I expect you to do
it." He had seized my arm and pulled me around till
we stood facing each other and I could see that he was
in a rage.

"Even if I think it oughtn't to be done?"

"An appendix it better out than in, isn't it?"

"Certainly, but——"

"Don't be a fool. How am I going to look before patients
if I tell them they need an emergency and then you come
along and say you want to wait and see, maybe it's not an
appendix, but something else?"

"Not so good, I reckon. But why do you tell them in
advance?"

"Because they want to know, in the first place; and in
the second place they don't think you're much of a doctor
if you can't tell them what ought to be done without waiting for the surgeon."

"I don't get it," I said. "If you had it your way, surgeons
wouldn't need to know anything about differential
diagnosis. They'd only have to be operators."

"That's what most of them are, aren't they?"

"Not by a long shot, at least not those I know. But tell

me, why do you call your surgeon to the house at all?"

"Chiefly to let the people see who you are and sort of size you up."

"Not really!"

"Yes, really."

"You don't want his opinion?"

"Not if it disagrees with mine in acute cases, generally speaking. It's a bit different in the others."

George was a mature man who had an enormous practice among the middle classes. Within limits he was very good, and nothing was too much for him to do for his patients. From time to time he gave me considerable work, but I noticed that each time I delayed operation or didn't do it at all, he sulked and for a time left me alone. Never before had he been so outspoken, but it was a desperately hot night and I suppose he was off his guard. Anyhow, we had it out.

"I think you make a terrible mistake," I told him. "And how any self-respecting surgeon can work under such conditions is beyond me."

He turned on his heel and left, saying over his shoulder: "You'd be surprised!"

I related that episode to Gus Henkel a week or so later and asked him what he made of it.

"Nothing that you would understand," came his prompt reply, but he smiled and I knew he didn't mean it unkindly.

"Come, now, what do you make of it and how could I have done differently? I'd never seen the Obermeyers before in my life and they were paying me for my opinion of their child's illness. Even if they weren't paying me, what difference would it have made once I came to see their child professionally? How could I have sent that child in and removed his appendix if I didn't think that was the thing to do? And why should I, the consulting surgeon, have regard for the feelings and wishes of the physician who called me in? Goddamit, this business of private practice makes me sick."

"It isn't simple."

"Doctors won't let it be."

"Some of them won't. There are physicians who do not play that sort of game."

"Assuredly, but too many of them assume a proprietory attitude towards their clientele, and woe be to him who doesn't bow to it."

Gus smiled.

"Man alive, what people don't know about private practice as it is carried on these days! Especially surgery. Little they know that practically all the operative work a surgeon gets is referred to him by physicians and that, much too frequently, it is referred on the basis of friendship or business or both—not nearly so much as people think on the basis of ability. No wonder physicians call the turn; no wonder they can say to a surgeon: 'When I call you to see an appendix I expect you to do it,' and get away with it! Let a fellow not follow instructions and bang! He's out of the picture and another fellow comes in who will do as bidden."

"I guess you think it would be better if we had socialised medicine," said Gus, with a laugh.

"No, I don't, or not necessarily; but I do think it would be better if surgeons weren't in private practice."

"You mean you would not have any surgeon—like yourself, for instance—practice as a private individual to be called into consultation for a fee by physician or patient or to operate on a private patient for an individual fee?"

"That's it exactly."

"But that's revolutionary!"

"Evolutionary would be the better word, Gus, but it's bound to come."

"How would surgeons live? Go on, explain yourself. Sounds too fantastic."

"I'd have all surgeons members of hospital staffs or members of groups of doctors and they'd go on call as they do now for practising physicians, whether members of their own hospital or group or not, and they'd operate, too, on private patients—but, and here's the main point, they'd have nothing whatever to do with the financial side of it. Their hospitals or groups would do all the billing and the money received would go into the general kitty, they themselves being salaried men."

"But why take only surgeons out of——"

"Because they are the keystone of so much in medicine that has dynamite potentialities."

"Are you joking?"

"No, I'm serious. And I propose that all surgeons be placed in exactly the same position that scientists are now—full-time salaried men who, having no financial interest in patients they see and maybe operate on, can be themselves—free men."

Henkel sat there staring.

"Shakes you, doesn't it?"

"It does indeed."

"And I'll go even further. I'd permit no choice whatever of one's surgeon by free patients or pay patients. The only choice I'd permit would be choice of hospital or clinic or group, the rest being entirely up to the chief of staff or the hospital's method of allocating cases to that man or those men best qualified to deal with them."

"You've got it all worked out, haven't you?"

"Bet I have, and all this fee-splitting, all this domination of surgeons by physicians, in short, all the unfortunate things in surgery that men on the inside deplore would disappear over night—by magic."

It was as if I'd exploded a bombshell.

"I'm a believer in freedom, Henkel, God knows," I went on, "but there are some things that have to be controlled, and surgery is one of them. The people cannot know and they've got to be protected. That is common humanity."

"Any idea how you'd manage it and pay for it? And how about the surgeons? Would they agree?" Henkel was practical-minded, to say the least. That was one of the reasons I liked him so much.

"The older ones probably wouldn't, the financially entrenched, but I believe the younger men would and lots of the middle group, too, because I'd pay them what they are worth, and they are worth a great deal. In fact, I think this whole business of full-time medicine is badly managed financially. If you want good men in business, in any walk of life, you've got to pay them adequately, and the better they are the bigger the money. It should be no different in medicine, but it is. Look at the scientists and see how niggardly they are paid—they to whom society owes so much. Look at the salaries of the professors of medicine and surgery in medical schools and of their assistants. It's silly.

"I'd put medicine on a business basis—bringing in business men if need be for the purpose—and I'd make private individuals and society, meaning municipalities, pay for value received, all monies going into the common fund. Thus all medical men connected with hospitals or groups on full time, surgeons included, would earn good money, comparable to the earnings of men in other walks of life. I see no insuperable difficulties about the matter unless it might be the doctors themselves. They fight obvious trends too much and seem unable to take the long view.

"What doctors need most and urgently is emancipation —emancipation from a social order that is dead. They are free scientifically. If they could only see that the scientific and the social go hand in hand and that neither can attain fulfilment alone."

19

TIME OUT FOR MEDITATION

ABSTRACT THINKING IS SOMETHING FEW DOCTORS INDULGE IN —they haven't the time—but it may not be amiss to suggest that the habit could be cultivated and, once formed, might be highly productive. Look at the things we ought to do something about and don't. Look, for instance, at the way we keep on letting every medical student decide what kind of doctor he wants to be and be it, without one word of guidance from anyone, without knowing or even considering whether he's fit for it or would be a better doctor if he went into some other field, without consideration by him or anyone else of the needs of the situation. It's hard to believe we've done much good thinking on this matter.

Freedom is a wonderful thing, but medical education is a long, arduous and expensive business; not everyone who wishes to ought to or can undertake it, and nothing about it ought to be held lightly. We have only the vaguest idea about how many doctors the people of cities, towns, and country districts require, and, so far as I know, none about how many general surgeons are needed, and nose and throat men, obstetricians, gynæcologists, and such. We ought to have that information, but we never thought of it or made serious effort to get it. And it's perfectly well known that recent medical graduates flock to the cities and won't go to towns and hamlets and into the country. Not for them the wind-swept plains and the hard work, long hours, solitude, and meagre pay!

So what we have is a faulty distribution of doctors, with people of the metropolitan areas over-doctored and people of the rural districts under-doctored (I'm not talking of the war years); and who but the medical profession should be concerned about that and take the lead in straightening it out? It's got to be straightened out, hasn't it? And if we don't do it ourselves somebody else will do it for us, and since that somebody else will probably be the government, many of us won't like it.

The first thing we ought to do, it would seem to me, is try to determine exactly what the needs of medicine are, metropolitan and otherwise, and with that knowledge formulate some method of meeting those needs—even if that means some restriction of youngsters' freedom of choice, even if it means, as it probably will, government help, particularly government money. You can't keep on having doctors falling all over each other in the cities while sick people of the country districts can't get one for love or money, because they aren't there to be had. And even the dullest among us will admit that hospitals are needed just as much in the remoter areas as they are in big cities. I grant that it isn't a simple problem, but that shouldn't prevent us from putting our minds to it—in force.

Then, too, the idea of giving a man so much freedom of action with few questions asked, just because he's got an M.D. degree and has passed his State Boards, has got to be looked at afresh. Medicine has progressed too far and become too involved and too potentially dangerous to permit it. People may have to be protected even against themselves. Hospitals of the better class restrict doctors to what they can do. Hospitals of a different character aren't so particular. There is no supervision whatever of a doctor's office or private practice!

Take surgery. I come back to that because I know most about it. A little man with ideas of grandeur and no sense of proportion goes to a famous clinic and sees a highly skilled, experienced surgeon take out half of a man's stomach apparently with a simple twist of the wrist, and follow that up with a couple of goitres. Maybe he'll do a couple of breasts, too, and take out a gall-bladder—quickly, deftly, all the time talking and firing the little man's ambition to emulate such deeds. And he does just that when he gets home, only with him it's not the simple twist of the wrist, and his patient does badly or dies. Isn't that a tragedy and oughtn't we to find some way of preventing it? Couldn't we, if we thought it through and tried hard and perhaps reached a clearer understanding of freedom in this matter and the limits thereof? The American College of Surgeons' supervision and restrictions are insufficient.

And suppose someone comes forth with a new idea, a bigger and better operation, a new drug. Is the little man capable of evaluating it? Is there any restriction on his going right out and trying it, willy-nilly the minute he gets hold of it, even though his patient does badly—or even dies—because it wasn't indicated in his case? Do you call that freedom? Must we continue to permit such transgressions, on the theory that to restrict the doctor's freedom of action would mean his enslavement? Couldn't we work out some airtight system of strict accountability? People are helpless because they are medically ignorant; they've been sold a bill of goods about choosing their own doctor by nobody else but ourselves. What do they know about a doctor's ability except through hearsay and how can they judge of his results if they don't know what his results are? How can we, ourselves, if we don't know them? And we don't, do we? How can we, if doctors in private practice never have to report their results—to anyone, to any agency? "Old Doc Jones brought all my children and now he is bringing their children," says Mrs. Brown. "He's the best obstetrician in the world." But is he? Does anyone know how many mothers, how many babies he's lost? Does he himself? It's the most ridiculous thing in the world. A man can go ahead and lose people's lives and no questions asked, but I'd like to see him lose their money.

I have no objection to the bigger and better idea, the new operation, the wonder drug. Heavens, no. I'm all for them. But the responsible groups assigned to try them out* ought to maintain controls indefinitely and no doctor anywhere, in or out of a hospital, should have the right to use those designated as dangerous without first registering at a suitable agency and later sending into that agency, in writing, a record of his results. Life is too precious and people are too much at the mercy of doctors for any other course.

There is no question that surgical transgressions would diminish if surgeons ever gave up private practice, but though I preach that and hope and believe it will come, it is a long way off. So, too, is the better education and training of surgeons and their coming up to the standards of the present American Board of Surgery. I'm even willing to agree that making men register and report their results indefinitely is too practical and logical to be invoked early, but that doesn't prevent me from thinking about it and making suggestions and calling for discussion.

But there's another and more subtle thing that has long been in my mind. It concerns what I call the "defeatist attitude" in surgery, and is reflected in the many and

* The American Medical Association does have a Council on Pharmacy and Chemistry, and lately the Council has established the Therapeutic Trials Committee. Splendid work is done in testing out new and untried things, and during the trial periods restrictions are clamped on. Only authorised doctors and hospitals can make the trials. The trouble comes when things are released.

different kinds of removals, the preponderance of amputations and excisions, on the general surgeon's calendar. He's always taking things off or out, rarely building them up, never putting them back. Did you ever think of it yourself? I have, many times, and it always has been disturbing. I wonder if we surgeons aren't too quick on the trigger both in our judgment and in our actions. Think of the appendices we remove and the breasts and gall-bladders and thyroid glands. Look at the legs and arms we amputate —and the pelvic organs of women we take out. Over half of our work, maybe more than that, is removal. The whole trend is towards removal. For a long time we did conservative surgery for stomach ulcers, but now we are hell-bent for the radical removal of the offending organ. Grandiose operations have been conceived and perfected for that purpose, with great pæans of acclaim for the masters whose minds conjured them up. I grant that radical surgery of the stomach seems to give better results that conservative, but I wonder if we have tried as hard to develop the conservative as we have the radical.

And now we're after lungs. We weren't surgeons enough to go for them in earnest before and had to be content with other treatments, but now we've learned, and out they are coming. It seems that whenever the art and science of surgery advance we look for things to sacrifice. Maybe that's right. Maybe it's for the best, but one can't escape the feeling that in many cases amputation, removal, elimination is not the answer unless as a confession of failure.

Suppose you do cure ulcers of the stomach by taking out the stomach. What does that prove and who wants to be without a stomach? Do you think a man can live happily without a stomach? He can with one-half or one-third, but then he's always liable to have another ulcer. So why keep on with that line of thought—which in the last analysis is defeatist? In the old days amputations and excisions were about all we could do, and we were glad to accomplish even those safely; but it would seem that now we could get beyond that if we'd try and maybe condition ourselves to a changed attitude of mind. I sometimes think surgeons accept with too great complacency the physician's decision that he has reached the end of his rope, and instead of reviewing with him the medical measures that have been taken with the patient and possibly pointing out others that might be tried, they proceed at once to operation, which is too often a removal. It is true that the medical men ought to know all the medical measures and how and when and to what extent they should be used. True, too, that the best ones do; but any man, good or bad, can make mistakes or overlook things of importance. Of course operating is the surgeon's business, and he'd hardly be human if he made a practice of foregoing operations; it may well be, too, that physicians would resent his questioning their decisions. Some of them are slow enough now about calling the surgeon and would like nothing better than a good excuse to be slower. Obviously, the matter is not simple or easy, but it does look as if too many surgeons hastily accept too many physicians' decisions, and to that extent at least there might be a change.

So much of surgery is concerned with cancer and so much cancer is late by the time it reaches us. That is one of the big reasons, perhaps the chief one, for our defeatist attitude. We are afraid of cancer, and rightly so. Cancer is one of the biggest killers of the human race. We don't know what starts it or what keeps it going, and we have little means of defence except to cut it out by the roots. X-rays and radium are helpful in the early, superficial ones, but, unfortunately, so many aren't superficial and unfortunately, too, cancer so often doesn't hurt in its early stages, and people don't get scared. Pain and fear bring people to doctors quickly, and we don't get either in early cancer, generally speaking. Hence much of the delay.

So it's easy to see why we rush in with knives swinging and no compromise. It's easy to see why we do the same in cases that are suspect. Prevention has come to be our watchword, and it is well. I admit that throughout the years I have been as ruthless and uncompromising with cancer and cancer suspects as the others; but it never set just right, and in the back of my mind there was dissatisfaction and doubt. I believe that we maimed and disfigured too many people—and lots of them we didn't cure, much less even than fifty per cent.

This tendency to removal is all so bad for the students of medicine and the young doctors, and if you think it isn't reflected in their attitude of mind, you're mistaken. Just a little while back, I was demonstrating a badly swollen, ominous-looking leg of an elderly diabetic. There were two open areas on the foot, serious infection was present and had not begun to be controlled—neither had the diabetes. After some talk I asked one student what he thought should be done.

"Amputate," came the prompt reply.

"Anybody else got any ideas?" I asked.

"You could treat her," vouchsafed one timidly, and then added: "But I don't think it would do any good."

"Why not?"

"Too far gone," put in a third.

"You mean you wouldn't make an effort to save the leg?" I queried.

"In the first place," said the second student, "it would take a long time to accomplish anything by conservative means, and in the end you might fail."

"All of which is quite true," I replied.

"So why try?"

"But don't you see that without knowing it yours is the defeatist attitude? I can't say that I blame you for taking it because we who teach you do too little to combat it. But just put yourselves in this woman's place and think whether you'd want an effort made to save your leg, even if it failed. Would you, son?" I asked of student No. 3.

"I guess I would, at that."

"This much you must see: you'll never save a limb or anything else if you don't try. The easiest operation in the world is amputation of a leg, and it doesn't take much of a surgeon to do it. Takes but a few minutes, a much shorter time than it does to grow one. On the other hand, it requires the highest surgical skill to save a leg, but even the long shots like this case sometimes fool you and reward your efforts."

I think surgeons especially should prepare for coming developments. For example, there is already in use a substance called thiouracil,* which makes certain types of toxic goitres fade out with great rapidity. It is not certain that it can effect a cure; in other words, the goitre tends to return if the drug is stopped; but it has been of inestimable aid in preparing desperately ill patients for operation, and it definitely points to new possibilities. If thiouracil doesn't

* Another and newer product is radioactive iodine, the result of the Atom Bomb research. X-ray is making greater strides in goitres and certain other conditions.

cure goitres, something else like it soon will, I have no doubt, and surgery in that condition will then be a thing of the past, as it largely is now in tuberculous glands of the neck and in varicose veins, just to mention two conditions.

In order to combat the defeatist tendency, I would make a beginning by saying to students and doctors alike, who come to watch operations: "This removal about to be done is the best we can do at the moment; in other words, amputations, extirpations, sacrifice of organs, should be regarded in the light of temporary expedients and we should all direct our minds towards methods of salvation and restoration. No man can say just when newer developments will make sacrifice unnecessary; but surely they will come. One may be permitted to be that much of an optimist, at least."

And I'd go further than that. In fact, I have. I have always refused to subscribe to removal of the stomach or part thereof until every possible medical aid had been exhausted, and there was no other way out. You might say, and with truth, that this is true of all good clinics; but you still find too many surgeons impatient. You find too many people who have stomach ulcers impatient also, so that they urge surgeons to operate, feeling that they'd much rather get the quick, positive relief that comes with surgery than undergo the long, uncertain relief by medical means. But it doesn't always work out happily even in the best of surgical hands, while in those that are average or poor it is even less satisfactory. And, of course, the operation has a definite mortality—low in the better clinics, not so low in the others.*

It is interesting and encouraging to note certain constructive developments—like the decreasing incidence of amputation for circulatory disease of the extremities once we realised that the use of tobacco was definitely a causative agent, and once we discovered that sympathetic nervous system imbalance had something to do with the condition. True, we take the nerves out, but that is much less destructive than taking the limb off. We have many nerves and they have a way of regenerating or making detour connections. Arms and legs don't grow back.

Recently, too, we've found that something can be done to prevent stopped-up veins (thrombosis) by the use of a substance called heparin and another called dicumarol. Nothing spectacular or one hundred per cent, but advance, progress, a straw in the wind. And, of course, the press has been loud in praise of the war surgeons who have saved so many more lives and limbs than had been expected. With their plasma and blood, sulfas and penicillin, they could delay operation and control infection and invoke more conservative measures. Who would deny that they will now be less defeatist and in all probability will impress their views on patients and doctors alike on their return to civilian practice?

The ophthalmologists can now transplant bits of clear cornea and thus give sight to the blind of the opaque cornea; the orthopædists think more and more in terms of restoration and each year perform more miracles; the gynæcologists do likewise to a considerable extent, though not sufficiently. It's easy to take the pelvic organs out; I know of one young surgeon who went to such excesses of this sort that the hospital took away all his surgical

* Recent work on the stomach innervation (vagus nerve) is pointing to less destructive methods in dealing with stomach ulcers. *See* Dragstedt, Lester R., "Vagotomy for Gastroduodenal Ulcers." *Annals of Surgery*, 122, 973–89, Dec. 1945.

privileges. Another hospital restored them, and that's the way it usually goes. Few men who have private patients ever lack a hospital wherein to work. Here, too, is a problem that cries out for attention and forthright action.

Everyone knows about the plastic surgeons and the miracles of restoration they work. You have only to look at the war veterans to see that, but, in the nature of things, plastic surgeons were always less defeatist than other surgeons. Some of the things they do are hard to believe. Whether it's a nose that was disfigured, a lower jaw that was shattered by shell-fire, or a contraction due to a burn, it matters little; they plug away doing five, ten, maybe thirty operations on the same patient in the search for perfection. Nothing of impatience there, nothing of defeatism.

It is the general surgeon who needs to take a fresh look at himself and his work, for he is the man who does the bulk of all the surgery; he is the man who is the backbone among surgeons. He really is the leader, and with good reason. He is the No. 1 trouble-shooter. To him come the acute things, the terrible things, the ones that try the soul and demand quick thinking, quick action, and sound judgment. It is the general surgeon, usually, who is chief of the surgical staff of hospitals and who selects house officers and is chiefly responsible for their training. It is he who does most of the appendices, most of the abdominal surgery—and there is a great deal of it—the ruptures, breasts, thyroids, amputations, big tumours and little tumours, cancer.

Throughout the years he has been chiefly a destructionist. It's amazing the number of organs and appendages the human body can get along without; in fact, that is probably a great part of the trouble. The surgeon knows his patient can do without his appendix and without his gall-bladder, without most of his thyroid, one kidney, both legs, even both eyes. He doesn't have to think about that part of it, and he doesn't to any great extent. He just follows the green light of routine and general custom. Perhaps this is not entirely wrong at the present time because the surgeon's first consideration is to save life, but I do not believe it is always for the best interests of the patient. In short, it seems to me that general surgeons, through force of circumstances—and habit—have become too much conditioned to the defeatist attitude in their work and need badly to be roused to a different attitude of mind even if it isn't possible to do very much on the restorative or salvation side at the moment.

I call to mind the increasing popularity among genito-urinary surgeons of the trans-urethral electric knife opera-tion for enlarged prostate glands, a procedure that requires less hospitalisation and is apparently less dangerous in the hands of experts than is the complete removal of the gland by operative means. True, this is not an operation for the average general surgeon, yet once again it points the way; and I cannot help feeling that if he began to think more in terms of salvation it wouldn't be long before he, too, came through with more new developments that would put him among the builders.

To save life is the first duty of a doctor; to prevent and alleviate suffering is the second. I would be the last man to say that the general surgeon hasn't done yeoman service in both, but his methods have been primitive to say the least, and continue to be so in spite of all the great advances medicine has made. I would not for one minute think that possible loss of their field actuates responsible surgeons in their continued defeatist attitude, any more than I believe surgery will ever become a lost art. We may well see the day, however, when there will be less general surgery. Think what would happen if cancer were prevented or cured by the "needle", as it might be. Think of the blow to surgery if appendicitis with all its sequelae was ever prevented or cured by medical means. We don't need to think of the inroads made on general and special surgery by the sulfas and penicillin; they are already here and still greater inroads may be expected as newer and more wonderful things are discovered. Plastic work, reconstruction, restoration, transplantation, accident work and such will be done in volume and will call for the highest surgical endeavour. But the removal of lungs, stomachs, thyroids, and other important organs of the human body then will be comparatively rare, and surgeons will talk of their "defeatist, primitive days".

I once knew a man who did a lot of thinking about surgery. He had been a cocaine addict in his younger days, and by the time I knew him he was the queerest, most aloof individual you could imagine. He had married but had no children. Few people knew him at all well, fewer intimately. He and his wife led a quiet, secluded life, one of their few attachments being a couple of dachshunds. I can't say he was my type of man—or anybody else's, for that matter—but he had charm when he turned it on, and we all knew he was a thinker even if we couldn't always make him out. And he was a most kindly man.

His name was Halsted—W. S. Halsted—whom you have met in these pages as "the professor". He became a cocaine addict from experimenting on himself. He and three other young, brilliant doctors did their experimenting during the course of certain investigative work and, according to the story, the other three died the usual miserable deaths. Halsted was saved by his close friend Welch *—also a great medical thinker. Welch took him to Europe and elsewhere and somehow broke him of the habit for good, not, however, before Halsted had given to the world the present-day method of block anæsthesia so widely used in dentistry—an epoch-making contribution in itself.

Halsted, first professor of surgery at the Hopkins, was a great surgical philosopher, but few knew just how great he was because he was so meek and humble and retiring. I dare say his cocaine experience had something to do with it. But of course we students knew nothing about that; nobody did, outside of Welch and two or three others, until Halsted's death, when his biographer told of it. So you can't blame us students for thinking the old gentleman somewhat "touched" and can perhaps understand why we never liked to be called down from the clinic benches to be quizzed by him on the patients he had before him—usually each Friday at twelve noon. He was kind and pleasant and didn't ride anybody, but he did ask the queerest, off-centre questions you ever heard. They all concerned surgery—or we thought they did—but very often they were on nothing we'd ever heard of, and few of us could ever fathom what the intent was. It was most embarrassing and uncomfortable.

I don't think he expected us to answer. Often he didn't give us a chance, but just went on talking as if to himself, as if thinking out loud, absorbed, hardly cognizant of the fifty or hundred students, doctors, nurses, and visitors sitting around him. Those of us there in "the bull-pen" stood

* Dr. William H. Welch, professor of pathology at the Hopkins and its guiding spirit for many years. A bachelor and the most erudite of men, he was familiarly known throughout the profession as "Popsy".

first on one foot then on the other, hardly taking in a word, waiting for the hour to be over—and wondering how much money there'd be in the kitty to divide among us. Each Friday, to solace the feelings of those who got called, each member of the class—except a few dignified ones—put ten cents in the kitty, and this dollar or two was balm indeed.

Not until I had been a graduate in medicine some years and had become a member of Halsted's staff was I able to appreciate the professor's clinics. Other men had the same experience. Even then we couldn't always follow his line of reasoning, but I came to see that this wasn't the important thing. The important thing was the stimulus the great man gave us, the fire he put into our less imaginative and less able brains—yes, even the dissatisfaction.

I can't imagine what Halsted would have thought of present-day medical problems or if it would have occurred to him to think of anything but pure, unadulterated surgery. But if he had, if the man whose brain gave us the rubber gloves all surgeons use today, and so much of our goitre and breast and blood-vessel surgery, if that man could have delved into the reasons for medicine's high concept of scientific needs versus its low concept of social needs, the extraordinary strides made in the one compared to the slow, halting, devious steps taken in the other, if he could have become convinced that the time had arrived for surgeons to give up their defeatist attitude, something of real and lasting value might well have come forth. For Halsted could think—and he knew better than most men that surgery is more than operations.

A surgeon who came in by the back door could hardly be expected to reach Halstedian heights, but no one can blame him for trying.